HITTING YOUR HEAD
AGAINST A BRICK WALL

HITTING YOUR HEAD
AGAINST A BRICK WALL

A surgeon's account
of raising concerns
in the NHS and why
the system needs
to change

Michael Swinn MD FRCS
Consultant Surgeon

Hitting Your Head Against A Brick Wall is a heart-felt and harrowing account of one person's struggle to keep patients at the centre of good medical practice, even when the system was constantly working against them. It is a "must read" for all medical students to empower them to be advocates for patient safety and speakers of truth to power should they ever find themselves in a similar situation.

Professor Claire Sharpe, Dean of Education,
School of Medicine, University of Nottingham

Michael Swinn undoubtedly saved lives by his struggle to get his concerns heard and if senior Trust executives learn from his experience and implement his recommendations, the impact on patient safety will be felt right across the NHS.

Lorcan Woods, ex-Chief Financial Officer,
King's College Hospital NHS Foundation Trust

Patient C was my husband; a kind, gentle and generous man who did not get to see our boys' marriages, successful careers or the birth of our grandson. We owe Mr Mike Swinn a debt of gratitude for his immense integrity and persistence in raising patient safety concerns. The negative reactions he faced deeply impacted both him and his family. As a former nurse I ask that every NHS service manager, clinician and board member read this book and act on its recommendations. It is sadly too late for our family but the issues he raises are a matter of life and death.

Widow of Patient C

I have had the privilege of working with Mike as a Consultant colleague for two decades now. In this very well written and emotive book he eloquently describes his role in the battles we faced for more than half of that time in trying our best to protect our patients. We should all look at learning the lessons that the events in this book teach us.

Professor Abhay Rane OBE FRCS, Consultant Urological Surgeon,
Surrey and Sussex Healthcare NHS Trust

This "unputdownable", well written book is a tough read on the pitfalls of being an NHS whistle-blower. It is shocking to hear how hard Michael had to push against so much resistance to be listened to in order to keep patients safe, and sad to hear of the huge personal cost. My practice as an NHS GP has already changed in response to reading this book and I would highly recommend it.

Dr Charlie Woodhams, GP

The extraordinary thing about Mike Swinn's book is that it isn't extraordinary. It is believable and recognisable; a healthcare tale that really belongs on the shelves marked "horror" or "crime".

Mr Tim O'Brien MA DM FRCS, Consultant Urological Surgeon, Guy's and St Thomas' NHS Foundation Trust and former President of the British Association of Urological Surgeons

Whistle-blowing in the NHS is sadly a very risky thing to do and it takes an exceptional person with enormous courage, integrity and dedication to do it, and to keep going for over a decade. Mike has all these qualities in abundance and it has been a privilege to work with him for the last twenty years.

Fellow whistle-blower, Surrey and Sussex Healthcare NHS Trust

An absolute page turner and utterly compelling, Hitting Your Head Against A Brick Wall highlights the perils of becoming a whistle-blower in the NHS and how the system needs to improve. Essential reading for all hospital doctors and managers

Professor Stephen Langley MS FRCS, Consultant Urological Surgeon, Royal Surrey NHS Foundation Trust

The current run of NHS scandals shows no sign of abating, with the Nottingham midwifery inquiry ongoing, the Thirlwall and Lampard inquiries due to commence shortly and further disturbing reports from Birmingham, Sussex, Newcastle and so on. In this context Michael Swinn's welcome new whistle-blowing book and Steve Bolsin's introduction both serve to remind us how little progress has been made with NHS safeguarding and speaking up over the last quarter century, and how much further we still have to go to render our NHS a safe place for staff and patients alike.

Mr Peter Duffy FRCS MD MBE, ex-Consultant Urological Surgeon and Chair of the Healthcare group, WhistleblowersUK.

As a colleague in the same department, I witnessed the whole episode from start to finish and Mike needs to be sincerely thanked. Despite unhelpful managers, he managed to bring about an end to practices which were harming patients, while all the time preserving excellent working relationships with all parties, and carrying out his clinical responsibilities in an exemplary manner. In this book he identifies the weaknesses in the various NHS systems and processes he came across, dissecting them down to the bone like an expert in anatomy and his recommendations need to be taken on board.

Mr Mushtaq Shuja FRCS Dip Urology,
Consultant Urological Surgeon,
Surrey and Sussex Healthcare NHS Trust

To be confronted by outdated and self-protective attitudes may have come as a shock to Michael Swinn in his capacity as a Consultant Urologist working in the NHS, but I have encountered them all my life in professional football. We owe patients in the NHS, and those playing the national sport, a duty of care when they enter into our arenas and fail them when we don't.

I would like to thank Michael Swinn for sticking his head above the parapet and exposing practices that have no place in a modern sophisticated health service that claims to be the best in the world. We need more like him.

Garth Crooks OBE,
former Chairman of the Professional Footballers Association

I found reading this very troubling. As a former hospital Consultant, it had not occurred to me that management would not move things on if you reported something serious that needed changing. As I continued to read I couldn't believe how the saga went on and on for years, until ultimately the Trust declared the person seeking to put things right, an offender. But he stuck it out until the truth finally emerged.

In my opinion Michael Swinn emerges as a complete hero. And so now I believe the recommendations he makes for change, which include regulating hospital administrator training, should be examined very carefully by whoever the authorities are that can improve the situation, so that nothing similar ever happens again.

Professor Clare Fowler CBE, former Professor of Uro-Neurology,
National Hospital for Neurology and Neurosurgery

Hitting Your Head Against A Brick Wall is not just about the NHS. There are crucial messages here that must be adopted across all sectors. An organisation which does not have a mature approach to whistle-blowing will never be a place where people thrive, develop and enjoy their work. Tolerance of toxic behaviour or incompetence destroys culture.

Christopher Brocklesby,
(new) Chief Transformation Officer,
Post Office LTD

Mike and I both spent our research years at the Mecca of Uro-Neurology, the National Hospital for Neurology and Neurosurgery in London. We were well trained and many years later can reflect on how we have enjoyed our successful careers. At least that is what I thought until I read this book!

I found it extremely painful to read of the trials and tribulations of a successful surgeon and the surrounding team doing their best in a system that had lost its focus on patients. What troubled me most were the many sleepless nights that were endured and the effect of that on the mind and body of a surgeon while juggling the additional roles of administrator and family man.

There are many important lessons to learn from this book, which I recommend most sincerely. Please read it, reflect on it and learn from it. I most certainly have.

Finally, it takes considerable bravery to lay your heart open to the world. Mike is to be congratulated for doing that with grace, honesty and dignity.

Professor Prokar Dasgupta OBE MD FRCS,
Professor of Robotic Surgery and Urological Innovation,
King's Health Partners

This book is dedicated to the thousands of patients who, every year, suffer harm at the hands of the NHS, and to all those who are brave enough to raise concerns.

Foreword

"YOU CAN'T MAKE THIS SORT OF THING UP" was my first response to reading Michael Swinn's account of his experiences at the urology department of The East Surrey Hospital in Surrey and Sussex Healthcare NHS Trust. And I just could not stop reading the incredible story. The narrative is gripping and to me still very familiar. It is also alarming and unnerving because it contains so many similarities to my training and work as an NHS Consultant in Bristol. I felt so much frustration and sadness that at times I had to put the book aside. Michael encountered exactly the same old-fashioned, self-protective and ignorant attitudes from clinical colleagues, senior managers and executives as I did. But by now all of them should have known better. I find it difficult to believe that Consultants, medical managers, Trust executives and non-executive directors could have made so many wrong decisions and quite literally 'fatal' errors.

The ordinary, thoughtful NHS user and employee would have rightly concluded that the 'Bristol Heart Babies Scandal' of the 1990s, in which I was intimately involved, would have made the process of raising professional concerns about unit and individual performance much easier. I am devastated this is not the case. Sadly, this episode at East Surrey Hospital confirms that the same outdated attitudes, ignorance and self-serving approach that characterised the Bristol Scandal have continued to thrive in the NHS for decades without correction.

This intensely personal and at the same time wholly representative memoir details the difficulties that a highly qualified and committed consultant faced when he decided that an impartial review was required of a clinician's clinical performance in the NHS. The engrossing narrative demonstrates that although patient safety should be prioritised in an efficient healthcare system, exactly the opposite has become the norm for NHS hospitals and the NHS overall. This unacceptable behaviour is to the enormous disadvantage of conscientious, responsible NHS staff in all professions and even more importantly seriously endangers patients. In many cases such as Bristol, Mid Staffs, Morecambe Bay, the Countess of Chester and East Surrey Hospitals, these uncorrected and unsupervised behaviours led to the untimely death of patients, many of them children.

When he started his post as Consultant Urologist, Michael Swinn was imbued with an undeviating desire to do the best he could for the patients he managed. As he was promoted to the more senior position of Director of Urology this responsibility spread to encompass all patients treated by the department. He detected unwarranted variations in the quality of care provided by a colleague coupled with an obvious conflict of interest. His reasonable request for an impartial review was ignored and resisted. The addition of concerns from cancer nurses and a Consultant colleague failed to persuade the hospital to take effective action until much later. Sadly, an eventual Royal College of Surgeons investigation and formal clinical review confirmed that poor care had caused much harm to many patients and a high-pressure Coronial investigation concluded that premature death was the outcome for some (no lessons learnt from the Mid Staffs Inquiry). Blame was appropriately apportioned and following a GMC hearing, the colleague in question with the conflict of interest was "struck off" the medical register.

The school of thought attributed to Aristotle defined four primary virtues that underpin any consideration of ethical behaviour. These are wisdom, conscience, temperance (moderation) and courage and were deemed to be pivotal to ethical motivation, subsequent decision making and resulting actions. In his protracted efforts to obtain initially a review, and eventually a restriction, on the suspected unethical practices in the Department of Urology Michael Swinn shows all of these primary virtues and is clearly motivated by and acting to the highest ethical standards. This leaves most of the other players in this sorry tale exposed to the criticism that their motivation, decisions and actions were at a far lower level, if not patently unethical.

Despite having been through such an appalling ordeal Michael has retained the detachment and foresight to produce a series of thoughtful and serious recommendations for clinicians and managers encountering similar circumstances in the future. Coming from a senior clinician and manager, who has such important first-hand experience these must be seriously considered by those in the NHS for whom this episode was an affront to patient care. This should include all clinical staff but must also encompass Trust and Department of Health executives and officials to enable them to identify and prevent similar future scandals in clinical care. If a practical approach to clinical safety and high-quality care is Michael's legacy from this disastrous episode of NHS management I am sure he will be most pleased. I had hoped for something similar from Bristol, but clearly it is yet to be effectively implemented.

Although some measure of justice was finally delivered, this in no way compensates Michael for the years of worry, work and wakefulness that this mismanaged scandal brought to him and his devoted family. The East Surrey Hospital staff and patients, the population served by The Surrey & Sussex Healthcare NHS Trust and the NHS in general owe Michael Swinn a large debt of gratitude for the commitment he has shown to high-quality patient care. Michael has helped ensure the highest standards of patient safety and the best possible outcomes for his patients, those of the East Surrey Hospital and all patients and relatives served by the UK's NHS. I for one would certainly like to thank him for that contribution, both formally and personally.

It is said that the only good thing about hitting your head against a brick wall is when you stop. Michael can stop now and through his lonely and tragic experience helps us make any repetition a redundant exercise.

Dr Stephen Bolsin

Acknowledgements

FIRST, I WOULD LIKE TO PAY TRIBUTE to numerous work colleagues who raised concerns alongside me, some of whom have suffered personally as a direct result. At the risk of offending some who are not mentioned here, I nevertheless feel compelled to highlight the actions of Clinical Nurse Specialists Kate Etheridge, Catherine Sharpe and Cathy Jenner. All three showed remarkable tenacity, clarity of purpose and compassion for patients, and showed what can be achieved by the simple approach of putting the patient at the centre of what we do.

Consultant Anaesthetist Dr Steve Bolsin has been described as "the gnawing conscience of the NHS" and is considered a trailblazer of whistle-blowing in healthcare. His actions in raising concerns about paediatric heart surgery at the Bristol Royal Infirmary in the 1990s led to the Kennedy report and to major clinical governance reform in many countries, including the United Kingdom. I am honoured, humbled and grateful that he has kindly written the foreword for this book.

I would like to thank British Airways Captains Martin Cantwell and Mark Ousey for their time in advising me on the changes made to safety in their industry in recent years. Also Emmanuel Ajayi, foreign exchange trader extraordinaire, at Standard Chartered Bank in Dubai for talking me through the strict conditions that now pervade his industry and the way in which speaking up about concerns is handled.

Many people encouraged me in this task. These include colleagues, relatives of those affected by the events described in this book, fellow whistle-blowers, including urologist Mr Peter Duffy

MBE, and other medics, including Professor Clare Fowler CBE. For everyone's support and advice I am extremely grateful.

Fraser Metcalf, copy editor, selflessly seemed to give up much of his Christmas correcting some of my syntax errors, pointing out my repetition and suggesting some tweaks here and there. My "test audience" kindly read my first full draft and reassured me that I was on the right track. I am grateful to all of them for invaluable feedback, including Kate Etheridge and my consultant colleague Mr John Grabham FRCS. I am grateful to solicitor Nicola Thatcher at Keystone Law for ensuring I stayed the right side of libel law and Alison Barker for her expert proofreading.

Finally, I would like to thank my amazing wife, Lesley, and our three remarkable children for their steadfast support, understanding and forbearance through many difficult years. They were forced by chance to observe at close quarters the ramifications of raising concerns in the modern NHS.

Contents

Introduction

THE EXPERIENCE OF WAKING UP TO NEWS of yet another NHS scandal has become part and parcel of modern life in the United Kingdom (UK). The deaths of babies at the Bristol Royal Infirmary, the Mid Staffordshire Hospital scandal where neglect led to more than four hundred excess deaths, the Morecombe Bay maternity scandal, the four hundred and fifty-six deaths in Gosport War Memorial Hospital, the Paterson scandal; the list goes on.

The health care "business" is vast, uncoordinated, innately complex and fraught with risk. Inevitably, pockets of bad or dangerous practice will exist. Regrettably, many remain undiscovered by the NHS's underdeveloped clinical governance systems and come to light only when attention is drawn to them by staff or patients. Whistle-blowers are therefore of paramount importance. The problem is they are often not listened to. In fact, they are routinely ignored and some become victims of cynical back-covering and obfuscation.

For many years, I and my colleagues raised concerns about poor practice in our hospital. We were far from alone, with many concerns being raised in different quarters of the hospital. But the system we encountered was woefully incapable of listening to our concerns or acting on them effectively.

Despite multiple attempts and numerous specific examples being given orally and in writing, it took many years for the cogs of the hospital machinery to turn. When they did, they were slow, clunking and amateurish. By the time managers belatedly accepted that our concerns were valid, a great deal of harm had sadly by then been done to many patients.

Those in charge subsequently came under fire and sought to defend themselves. Part of their strategy in doing so was to try to discredit and devalue the testimony of the whistle-blower in the vain hope that "muddying the water" would divert attention elsewhere. Backed by the Trust's inexhaustible supply of legal help, they turned their firepower on to those who had raised concerns, creating an adversarial, acrimonious and unequal fight.

Despite my experience of more than thirty years as an NHS hospital doctor and Consultant Surgeon, this caused many dark days for me and my loved ones, and I reflect now on how this issue would have resulted in professional ruin had it not been for the support of family, friends and some good colleagues.

This book is not about any individual or individuals but, rather, a dysfunctional system, ill-equipped to deal with serious concerns, and one which showed its vindictive nature all too readily. It is written from the whistle-blower's perspective and, although many finding themselves in a similar position will have been subjected to far worse, the all-consuming nature, frustration and sense of isolation that go with raising concerns in the modern NHS will be all too clear. I hope that it might help those considering raising concerns, so that their own journey might be smoother and that the ultimate purpose of whistle-blowing – highlighting failings that affect real people, their families and their lives – will be advanced.

Anyone arguing for change does so more persuasively having experienced first hand a system so obviously ill-equipped to deal with the raising of concerns. This is *my* account, and the historian EH Carr's advice to "study the historian before you study the facts" is relevant here. For that reason, I spend some time during the first part of the book describing my early years in the profession. Some of the hiccups I experienced as a junior doctor are laid bare, but I hope that my values become clear – the importance of teamwork, communication and putting the patient at the centre of decision making.

The second part of this book describes how dedicated staff raised concerns on multiple occasions and examines the response from hospital management. The third part describes the seemingly interminable investigations and fallout after our pleas for help finally gained traction. The final part is an analysis of what in essence went wrong, accompanied by a brief comparison with other industries, which at the very least serves as a potent way of demonstrating the inadequacies of the NHS's systems and processes.

I finish with a list of recommendations, and I fervently hope that those in positions of power and influence will at least listen to these suggestions, and to those of the many others who, like me, have been in this situation. The evidence of scandal after scandal in the NHS sadly shows that radical change is long overdue and is so obviously highly necessary.

Notes on the text

Throughout the book, I refer to many individuals by their role or job title. This is for three reasons: first, to spare the blushes of those involved; second, to help avoid confusion since the post holders changed frequently; and lastly to emphasise my view that change must be brought about by focusing on systems rather than individual failures.

I made copious notes throughout this whole period and, when I use quotation marks in the text, these are frequently from contemporaneous notes, although some are from memory. Either way, they are intended to be an accurate record of the actual words used. Where quotation marks are used in reference to a particular investigation or legal process such as Coroner's court, or from emails or other digital forms of communication, quotations are employed directly from the transcript.

Olivia

IT IS A BRIGHT SATURDAY IN SPRING and my eighteen-year-old daughter sits at the kitchen table. She has bought a book on how to get into medical school and is now on the section dealing with the interview. She is going through possible questions, considering how best to answer them. Numerous pieces of paper are scattered on the table in front of her, seemingly in a state of disorderliness. I can see that each is adorned with copious scrawled notes in her own hand.

She looks up. 'Can I ask you a question?'

'Of course.'

'How do I answer it if they ask me what I would do if I had concerns about the practice of a fellow doctor? Do I just tell them I would tell the managers?'

'It's a bit more complicated than that,' I answer.

PART 1

Training

CHAPTER 1

Medical School

A RED TOWEL WAS DRAPED around his neck, tucked under long hair, and, as he sat down in front of me, I realised that the towel had in fact once been white and was now caked in blood. I gingerly lifted up an edge to investigate but was met with a gush of blood, and instinctively pushed back the sodden towel and applied some pressure.

'What happened?', I asked, trying my best to sound authoritative.

'The cutting machine broke and I went to check it and the blade came down on the back of my neck.'

So started my very first afternoon in the outpatient department of the Black River Hospital, St Elizabeth, in rural Jamaica. It was November 1990 and I was on my "elective" – a few-months' stint in which medical students go to generally far-flung parts of the globe to gain experience of another country's health care system and confidence in seeing patients. I had naively chosen the Caribbean, imagining it might be an easy option, but the reality was that I had been placed into a very busy hospital with dedicated but overworked staff. There were three "doctors": two real ones, Dr Mshana and Dr Bamidele from Ghana and Nigeria, respectively, and me, a final-year medical student from University College London.

Easing the man up from his chair to go into the operating room next door, blood now having dripped on to the floor, I started to feel faint. I turned to Sister Mary and asked if one of the doctors was around.

'No, Doc,' she replied.

I pointed out that I was just a medical student, hadn't seen anything like this before and asked her again; this time in a more pleading tone.

'Nobody here except you and me, Doc.'

We first sat him on the edge of the operating table and then swung his legs up. We then turned him over, his face pressed into a pillow, and Mary placed a second under his chest, pushing it up to allow better access to the back of his neck. She switched on the operating light and removed the towel to reveal a deep wound several inches long. At the very base of it, I could momentarily glimpse some spurting arteries before the wound filled with blood, obscuring the view entirely. As I stood up straight trying to clear my head and wondering what to do, Mary proffered a large jar of clear white fluid within which were floating numerous odds and ends of sutures of different types and sizes. All had seemingly been used before but were deemed to be of sufficient length to be stored for future use.

'What suture would you like?' she asked while unscrewing the lid.

I peered in and sniffed.

'What's the fluid?', I asked.

'White rum,' she replied.

. . .

Growing up, I had my fair share of trips to the family GP. First, Dr Savage, an elderly and kindly man, whose almost illegible handwriting was delivered by the most bizarre pen grip imaginable; the pen being clutched firmly between two fingers only, the thumb pointing uselessly out to the side. Although no more than seven or eight, this peculiarity fascinated me and, on questioning him, I was informed that his hand had been broken during a boxing match many years before and this was the only way he could now write. This impressed me very much and made me look forward to seeing him in his surgery in Southampton and, whenever I went, I imagined him adorned with a fine pair of black boxing gloves!

In time, he was replaced by Dr Wendy Johnson, who was equally friendly and welcoming. These two amazing GPs were the sum total of my direct experience of medicine while growing up, but they both left a lasting impression that they were doing something worthwhile and that they seemed to enjoy their jobs, and were shoo-ins on the annual list of those given a bottle at Christmas time.

Looking back on it, I think I had pretty much always wanted to be a doctor but hadn't verbalised it until a meeting with Ian Brownlie, my chemistry teacher, in September 1982. He doubled up as the school careers master, and one afternoon we met in his lab surrounded by Bunsen burners and flasks to discuss the future. He looked doubtful of my A level choices.

'Surely you should be doing arts A levels? Perhaps English, French and something else?'

'Well, if I did those then I couldn't do medicine.'

'So, you want to be a doctor?'

'Yes,' I replied, a little uncertainly.

It was the post O level discussion, and his point was valid. My science grades were borderline for an aspiring medic and, at least on paper, it would seem more sensible to pursue a different course. I have since wondered what the response would be now, in the age of league tables. I suspect a firmer line would be taken from those in charge and my medical career might have been aborted before it had started. Fortunately, 1982 was firmly pre league table and I was allowed to study A level maths, chemistry and biology.

Although I wasn't predicted top grades, my application was just about strong enough overall to be offered interviews at two of the five medical schools I had applied to, including my top choice, University College Hospital (UCH) London. I well remember trying to ignore the knot in my stomach on interview day as I crossed Tottenham Court Road from Goodge Street Underground station in search of Gower Street and UCH's Anatomy entrance. Going upstairs past the main lecture theatre, I found the door for the medical school office with a notice pinned to its outside: "Do not knock before entering. Please go straight in". Inside, I nodded a hello to a couple of other candidates and introduced myself to Gwen, the secretary behind the desk. As I did so, I was aware of someone seated in a shadowy corner surveying the scene. I subsequently realised that this was Dr John Foreman, Dean of Admissions, as it was he who interviewed me later that afternoon. I wondered afterwards whether he had surreptitiously positioned himself in the room to make an assessment of the candidates as early as possible by seeing if we had enough common sense to read the sign on the door and follow its instructions, and perhaps also to see how we interacted with Gwen. The interview went well and I was delighted when he telephoned me later that day to offer me a place starting in September 1985.

Medical school was almost entirely pleasurable. In halls in Camden I made some truly great lifelong friends, the work on the whole was interesting and, having established that when qualifying some five years hence there would be no grades awarded but merely a pass or fail, I early on actively made the decision to coast through the following six years. Thus, there was plenty of time to play golf, cricket and snooker; my habit being to knuckle down and work hard for the few weeks before each set of exams.

Following a traditional curriculum meant that pretty much every morning during the first year started with anatomy dissection. Nothing quite prepares you for the glare of the dissecting room, the smell of formaldehyde, the stinging eyes and the countless rows of cadavers. Mercifully, the heads were wrapped up – the lack of identity making it easier, especially during the first weeks when, six to a body, we picked up our scalpels and dissected our way through the thorax and abdomen, identifying the anatomy as we went along and doing our best to memorise the appearance of hundreds of blood vessels, nerves and other structures. Nauseatingly, the formaldehyde tended to cling to the fingers for the rest of the day despite repeated hand washing, but nevertheless anatomy quickly became my favourite subject and the six of us worked cohesively to make good use of the cadaver that had generously been donated.

In the evenings, we generally did a little work before going to the residence bar or local pub; a pattern that was to continue more or less unaltered for six years. The first two years were spent in the lecture theatre and tutorial groups, the third many of us spent doing an extra degree (I chose to do a BSc in the history of medicine) and the last three were clinically orientated, based largely on the wards of University College and the Middlesex Hospitals. Towards the end of clinical training, and shortly before finals, would come the student elective. In our eyes, this represented the climax to our training because it afforded an opportunity to go abroad and gain "hands-on" experience.

On occasions during the final three years, we were farmed out for fairly lengthy spells to various district general hospitals, including those at Eastbourne, Southend, Ipswich and Edgware. On these attachments as clinical medical students we did precious little actual work – mostly we observed – but they exposed us to a spectrum of specialities, we gained medical knowledge and learned essentially how hospitals work. Several of us were sent to these hospitals at the same time, and each of us was attached to a "firm": a well-defined team of doctors led by the Consultant. Under the Consultant was a Senior Registrar – the most senior of junior doctors, generally late thirties and always very experienced. These doctors had all but finished their training and seemed to spend much of their time going to Consultant interviews. The Registrar was next in the pecking order: a medic who had decided their particular speciality and who had already spent many years working their way well up the greasy pole. Then came the Senior House Officer (SHO) and finally the humble House Officer (HO); these last two grades being relatively newly qualified doctors. The whole group of doctors up to and including the Consultant constituted a firm and there was always a great team spirit and often a degree of healthy rivalry between firms.

•   •   •

But in Jamaica, on that first day, as I anxiously fished in the jar wondering what suture I could use, real, practical doctoring was proving a very new experience. Eventually, I found a few decent lengths of catgut and, with a nod of encouragement from Mary, took the plunge.

Even with her experienced assistance, every time the edges of the wound were parted, blood welled up from the base obscuring the view and making suturing impossible. I had never before been faced – or even seen – anything like this and looked up at Mary for inspiration. She made a sort of clamping gesture with her middle and index fingers pressed together and handed me a surgical clip. Waggling it in the blood at the base of the wound, I closed its jaws around some unseen tissue, hoping to have incorporated a blood vessel. Repeating the manoeuvre with more clips being pressed into my hand by Mary resulted, after a while, in a degree of control of the situation and eventually I could just about glimpse the base of the wound. Perhaps it was the white periosteum of the neck vertebrae reflecting the light.

Mary passed me a series of ties and I cack-handedly managed a knot of sorts around the tip of each of the numerous clips, allowing them to be removed one by one. Some had to be reapplied for a repeat attempt but, with great relief, the bleeding gradually subsided. I then put in some sutures – again amateurishly – but after a while the bleeding stopped altogether. I closed the muscle and finally the skin and, after applying a dressing, slumped into a chair to write up the patient's "docket" (clinical notes), thanking Mary profusely.

That evening, sitting in the Waterloo Guest House in Black River town eating my dinner, I reflected on the day's events and felt that, despite my stumblings, I had made a really positive impact on someone's life. In fact, arguably, I might even have saved it. I felt a sense of elation, even euphoria, at what I had achieved, and marvelled at the direct way in which surgery can affect a fellow human being, and the instantaneous reward it could have for the surgeon. I ran through the incident in my mind, wondering how I might have done better. Certainly, my knot tying should have been slicker, and I resolved there and then to practise my surgical knots at every opportunity, using any old piece of string or shoelace to hand.

Early the next morning, I met Dr Bamidele in the hospital kitchen and, when I walked in, was greeted a number of times with

'Morning, Doc' and 'Good day, Doc' by the hospital staff. They seemed insistent on calling me that despite my repeated protestations that I was in fact not a doctor at all but just a medical student. Dr Bamidele and I made our way to the very end of the kitchen where a single small table, laid for two, waited. We started talking about what my role would be in the hospital and had barely started breakfast when he was summoned to take a call on the kitchen telephone. After a brief conversation, he turned to me and said, 'Come on, let's go. We need to go to Casualty before the ward round.'

As we walked in, I almost fainted for the second time in two days. On the table, groaning in pain, was a man with such a badly broken leg that the sole of his foot had been wrenched more than ninety degrees to lie roughly parallel to his shin, with the ankle joint and two bones of the lower leg, the tibia and fibula exposed.

Dr Bamidele, seemingly entirely unfazed, asked the nurse to administer some morphine and fluid and, with that, he pulled the foot down, out and roughly in line with the rest of his leg as best he could, put a splint on and, having checked for a pulse in the foot, sent the man to the ward for theatre. I was utterly in awe of the extraordinary way in which Dr Bamidele was able to manage an emergency of this sort without so much as breaking stride.

After a mammoth ward round of the medical, surgical, obstetric and paediatric wards, I was introduced to Dr Mshana. He would do most of the operations in theatre, leaving Dr Bamidele primarily to look after the wards and outpatients. Discussions regarding my timetable resumed: I would breakfast in the hospital kitchen at 7.30 a.m., then ward rounds at 8 a.m., back to the kitchen for lunch, followed by outpatients or theatre in the afternoon. In addition, I would be on call every third night and every third weekend. The equivalence they gave me to a qualified doctor terrified me, but I realised I was being given an amazing opportunity to be part of a busy surgical team and would gain all sorts of valuable experience.

On my first evening on call I was just arriving back at my room when I heard 'Doc, Doc' through the wooden shutters. Elroy, one of the porters, had news of work for me to do. I made my way over to the outpatient/Casualty rooms where there were some emergencies to see already, including a teenage girl racked with pain. To begin with, I had absolutely no idea what was wrong with her but examination of her docket revealed a history of sickle cell disease. My mind drifted back to a young patient I had once seen in London in the midst of a sickle cell crisis. Luckily, I could remember how he was managed and duly prescribed morphine, intravenous fluids and oxygen.

I placed a tourniquet tightly around the girl's upper arm, and the cannula – essential for venous access to enable administration of the fluid and drugs – seemed to go into the back of her hand well. But when I turned the fluid on it would not run in. I concluded that I must have missed the vein and took it out. I tried again with a large cannula but got the same result. I tried again with a different cannula and different vein, but with the same result. The poor girl was screaming in pain and I was by now sweating profusely. If I couldn't get the needle in, what on earth would I do? I stood back and surveyed the scene. She had punctured arms now in several places with blood leaking from various sites. Given the screaming and amount of time I was taking, Sister Mary came through, muttering something about the number of cannulae I was going through. She took one look and with a "tut" removed the tourniquet on the patient's arm. I had inadvertently left it on with the result that it blocked the fluid from going in! As soon as she removed it, the fluid whistled in, now unimpeded. I clearly had a lot to learn, including the very basics.

It took me a few weeks to learn to pace myself for the long days and nights on call and, one day in early December, I allowed myself the luxury of going in just after 8 a.m. once I had showered, shaved and listened to the BBC World Service on the radio. Maybe I had a sixth sense that the next thirty-six hours would be traumatic.

The day passed peacefully enough, with the usual mix of cases that were commonplace in rural Jamaica but baffling to a medical student from London, such as a red, hot, swollen thumb belonging to an unlucky farmer (answer: scorpion sting).

I went to bed late that night, but was soon woken by Elroy. I turned on my torch and glanced at the clock – 3 a.m. I dressed, walked down the corridor to the communal bathroom and, trying to wake myself up, splashed some water on my face and made my way across the courtyard to Casualty. I sat down in the small office with moths and other insects circling the overhead light and read the docket before asking the patient in.

She was sixteen and described abdominal pain and bleeding. Both had started the previous evening and she didn't know why. She reported normal periods, no history of trauma, no boyfriend. I examined her carefully and was puzzled. There was what I took to be a swollen and hard uterus and some blood in the vagina. I asked her again about her periods and she was now more uncertain.

'I think you might be pregnant,' I said. 'Do you think that might be possible?', I continued.

'No Doc,' she said.

I was out of my depth and unsure what was going on, so I decided to put up a drip and admit her with a working diagnosis of "?Pregnant ?Aborting?" Dissatisfied, I made my way to bed and, after having to see another emergency at 6 a.m., overslept.

I joined Dr Bamidele in the kitchen for a bite to eat once he had finished the ward round and asked if he had seen the girl I had admitted in the night. He replied, 'Yes, although she's now on the maternity ward. Why don't you go and see them?' Them? I left my semolina and made my way across the path to the maternity ward.

As I entered, I met the maternity Sister in the doorway and asked what had happened. She explained that a few hours after I had admitted the girl, someone had brought in a newborn baby. They had heard crying from a bush, went to investigate and found a baby boy still with the placenta attached.

'What you were feeling was not a pregnant uterus but a post-partum one. It contracts and goes hard like that straight after birth.'

I felt very stupid. 'Where is she?', I asked and was gestured towards a door which opened into a small room with a bed, in which lay the young woman covered by a sheet and with a tiny baby boy in her arms.

I met Sister outside. 'Is he going to be alright?', I asked.

'He's struggling at bit, but he is close to full term,' she replied.

I left and went to clinic. The day dragged. I found it difficult to concentrate, and at the end I went back to the maternity ward but was prevented from going in. Lots of people were milling around, including a number of policemen in pristine, starched uniforms. No one was talking and the atmosphere was tense. Then I spotted the maternity ward Sister I had spoken to earlier and asked her what was happening. She was upset but collected herself, leaned forward and whispered, 'The baby died.'

I reeled back in shock. I don't think I replied, but I made my way down to the water's edge behind the hospital and sat watching the sunset, leaving only when I could take the mosquitoes no more.

I thought about that incident frequently over the following days and weeks and concluded that I had made a series of mistakes; not least of all by starting with completely the wrong diagnosis. I was sure that a more experienced clinician would have realised that the young lady had recently given birth and that efforts to locate the baby might have resulted in him coming to hospital sooner with a much better chance of surviving. Perhaps sensing my upset over the issue, my colleagues suggested a couple of days off over Christmas, which I gladly accepted.

• • •

Having retired a year or two before, Dr Francis was the elder statesman of Black River Hospital. He had been my initial contact and we had met a few times because he occasionally helped out in clinic. He kindly invited many of the hospital staff, including me, to his house for Christmas lunch. It was a blisteringly hot morning, which I spent walking into, and around, town. Having showered and changed when I got back to the hospital at noon, I embarked on the walk to Dr Francis's house.

I arrived slightly late to a fairly sizeable gathering and, as I was shown a seat, a particularly large glass of ice-cold Heineken was pressed into my hand. I had doubtless lost a lot of fluid during the morning and drank it quickly. The excellent hospitality meant that just as I drained it my glass was replaced with a full one. Dr Francis then offered me some Sorrel, a traditional Christmas fruit punch. There were copious ice cubes floating in it and it tasted fantastic. Still thirsty, I sipped steadily on it, convincing myself – wrongly as I later learned –that it wasn't particularly alcoholic. The delicious food was a welcome change from the fare I had encountered in the hospital kitchen, and the cold bottle of crisp white wine that appeared in front of me was a real treat.

After the main course, Mrs Francis uncovered a huge Christmas pudding and, above the general hubbub, I could just about make out a conversation about a coin. My tiredness, the heat, noise and by now my rather inebriated state were rather discombobulating and I thought perhaps I had misheard, and sought clarification. A beaming Dr Francis replied, 'Michael, it's a Jamaican tradition to have a coin in the pudding and whoever gets it has to sing a song.'

Oh dear, could he be serious? Mrs Francis lit the pudding and, holding up her hand, invited everyone to make a wish. I had no hesitation and, closing my eyes, muttered under my breath more of a prayer than a simple wish that the coin would end up in someone else's dish.

Mrs Francis came round serving the pudding and we all began eating. I picked up my spoon and, concerned that I might have been set up, nervously loaded it with just a small amount. All was well initially but before long disaster struck when my spoon picked up a small disc wrapped in silver foil. I froze and briefly considered returning it to the bowl to try and hide it under the remainder of the pudding. But it was too late! Dr Francis had spotted it and the general background noise was replaced first with silence and then with clapping as everyone realised that the coin had been located.

With people now banging on the table and cheering, Dr Francis implored me to stand and sing. The two obvious problems with this were that I cannot – *cannot* – sing but also I had by now had too much to drink for standing to be easily accomplished. Knowing I had no choice, I forced myself to rise slowly.

'What are you going to sing?' someone shouted. Oh dear, I hadn't even thought. I looked out at the smiling faces and realised with relief that they all seemed to have enjoyed the hospitality as much as me. A song recently heard on the radio came to mind and I began the Frank Sinatra classic 'And now, the end is near....' My mouth was dry and my voice croaky and out of tune, but somehow I managed to get through – more or less – to the bitter end and sat down, very gratefully, to sympathetic applause and inebriated cheering.

* * *

I learned that day that I enjoyed the social side of hospital life as well as the work, and I loved the feeling of being part of a surgical team in which we shared the good times as well as the bad. Dr Mshana and Dr Bamidele also helped ignite in me a passion for surgery, and I spent much of my remaining time in Jamaica in the operating theatre where Dr Mshana patiently answered my numerous questions and between cases drew diagrams to aid his explanations. The theatre backed directly on to the beach and the theatre door was commonly propped open. Thus, it was here, in rural Jamaica, that I learned suturing and other basic surgical skills, soothed by a cool sea breeze wafting through the theatre. Whether once back in the UK I would be prepared to embark on the lengthy, arduous training in order to become a surgeon would be a decision for another day. First, I would have to get through medical school finals in order to qualify and only then could I embark on the many years of hard work as a junior doctor.

I came off the beach early one evening in January to meet two new students, Andrew and Helen, from St Thomas', who were taking over from me. I could not believe how pale they were, nor how worried they seemed. Chatting about what their roles entailed and what would be expected of them did nothing to quell their anxiety.

'There's something else that really scares me,' Andrew said. 'They keep calling me Doc.'

'Don't worry, you'll get used to it.'

CHAPTER 2

House Officer years

RETURNING AT THE END OF JANUARY 1991 to a snowy UK, the world had changed in a number of respects. A tearful Margaret Thatcher had left Downing Street and been replaced by John Major, and the first Gulf War dominated the news with Operation Desert Storm in full swing. On leaving for Jamaica towards the end of the previous year, I had reluctantly given up my lovely Highgate flat and was lucky to get a place in self-catering halls of residence in Belsize Park for the few months leading up to finals in June. Many in my year had made the same decision and, at various times depending on the timing and duration of their chosen elective, moved into halls in the run-up to finals.

Sitting down by myself and studying has never come naturally as I get too easily distracted, but my room at the rear of the house was quiet and overlooked the house's large garden. During study breaks, we were inevitably drawn to the garden, which hosted some epic snowball fights, and between us we created a truly huge snowman adorned with facial features. When I looked up from my desk, the wintry scene reassured me that the summer exams must still be a long way off. I had clearly underestimated the vast amount of snow and ice we had packed into him because remnants could still be seen well into mid spring, and it was with some alarm that I realised, with just weeks to go before finals, that I was significantly behind in my revision timetable.

Surrounded by files of notes and weighty textbooks, panic could have set in, but having so many people studying for medical finals was very helpful because we were essentially all in the same boat.

We formed ourselves into a number of informal study groups where we discussed all sorts of topics, and also practised the process of taking a history and physical examination, using a stethoscope, tendon hammer, etc. When the time came to take the exams, it was a group activity – several of us would get the Tube together, enter the examination hall together and exchange looks of horror as we turned the paper over for the first time.

On results day, we all waited with trepidation in a pub off Mortimer Street by the Middlesex Hospital. Just after the appointed time (why are these things always delayed?), each of us grabbed our envelope and found a quiet corner somewhere to open it. There were yelps of joy, hugs, a few tears of disappointment among some of my friends but there were no major upsets and we returned to the pub transformed – now the proud possessors of MBBS after our names. Qualified doctors!

My year as an HO would start in Urology at the Middlesex Hospital. I would then rotate to general surgery at UCH before moving to Bath for six months to do cardiology. On 1 August 1991, I started at 8 a.m. sharp on Thomson-Walker ward at the Middlesex Hospital. I was one of a team of two HOs and quickly bonded with the other, Umraz Khan. We were expected to know all the patients on the ward well and to clerk them in for their operations, which meant taking a history, writing out their medication chart, consenting them for their operation and doing their blood tests. We also had to order any investigations, retrieve the results and present them to the Registrar, Sam Hampson, and the Senior Registrar, Chris Chappell, on the ward rounds held daily at 8 a.m. and 5 p.m.

It was an illustrious firm, with eminent Consultants Professor Richard Turner-Warwick, very recently retired, Mr Alf Cowie, Mr Ewen Milroy and Mr Peter Worth. The long days were made much more difficult because I also did a "one in three" with internal cover, so, in addition to working nine or ten hours every day, five days a week, I also was on call every third evening and night and every third weekend. This meant starting work at 8 a.m. one day and finishing at 6 p.m. the following day and, on weekends, starting at 8 a.m. Saturday morning and finishing at 6 p.m. on Monday. The internal cover bit meant that, when one of the two other people sharing the rota was away, the others would do their shifts for them in addition to their own.

Despite my experience in Jamaica having prepared me to a degree, the discipline of working hard and long hours took some getting used to, and some aspects were alien to me, for example, consenting patients for complex urological operations. This necessitated asking lots of questions of the more senior junior doctors and going to the library to learn as much about urology as I could. Although I did not realise it at the time, this would prove to be ideal training for a budding urologist. The other shock came at the end of the month when I got my payslip. The overtime hours (i.e. those in excess of forty per week) were grouped into lots of four with each called a unit of medical time (UMT,) and were paid at a third of normal rate.

I had never really got used to being woken up in in the middle of the night in Jamaica by Elroy or another of his colleagues and it was the same back in the UK – except that now it was the cursed bleep's shrill tone that would wake me. One night at about 2 a.m. I was called to see a young man of twenty on the ward. Mr Cowie had operated on his kidney the previous day to remove a large stone. The stakes were high because the patient only had one kidney. He had been back on the ward since early evening but hadn't recovered in the way the nurses had expected. I was living in hospital accommodation next to the hospital and so was on the ward within minutes of being called.

It was immediately clear with a glance from the foot of the bed that something was terribly wrong. He looked deathly pale, sweaty and was drowsy. His blood pressure had been low postoperatively but had dropped further over the last couple of hours and he had stopped producing urine. He needed urgent resuscitation and so I gave boluses of fluid through a drip, took bloods and, expecting him to be anaemic, ordered blood from the blood bank. Despite my interventions, he was deteriorating fast, so I decided to telephone Sam, the Registrar, who asked me to prepare the patient for theatre, and by 5 a.m. the patient was on the table. We started to reopen the wound by unpicking the sutures Sam had carefully placed the previous afternoon and, as we went deeper, the cause of the problem became clear – he was bleeding steadily from his solitary kidney. Removing the kidney would solve the problem and save his life but, if we did remove it, he would be on dialysis with all the limitations that would impose. Sam called in Mr Cowie, who appeared quickly, scrubbed up and joined us with a 'Good morning, gentlemen.'

In principle, it seemed a relatively straightforward task – cauterising and suturing over the bleeding points we could identify. In practice, however, it was proving nigh on impossible because every time a stitch went into the meat of the kidney it would pull through and cause even more bleeding. We were not winning and there were murmurs of having to perform a nephrectomy when Mr Cowie decided to try one last thing. Rather than putting conventional stitches in, with great skill he used a buttress suture over and over again to effect a sort of bunching-up of the kidney. I had never heard of this technique, let alone seen it, but after a while the bleeding reduced and we all started to relax a little. At about 7 a.m. the bleeding had stopped altogether, the anaesthetist had squeezed in many bags of the blood I had ordered earlier and Sam and I closed. When I saw the patient later that morning, he was much improved – sitting up in bed wondering what all the fuss was about!

Although my experience in Jamaica had sparked an interest in surgery, I was still undecided what to do for a career and in fact openly stated that my plan was to become a GP. However, the experience of that night at the Middlesex reminded me of some of the experiences in Jamaica and reignited a passion for surgery. Similar to my emotions when sitting in the Waterloo Guest House in Black River almost a year before, I thought how amazing and satisfying it was to help another human being so directly.

After that night, I made sure that I got to theatre as much as possible, staying late into the evenings to catch up on the day's work. I mostly watched Mr Cowie operate and, one day, a few weeks later, the next patient had just been put to sleep on the operating table when Mr Cowie turned to me and said, 'Have you ever done an inguinal hernia repair?'

'Er, no', I replied, laughing, as I had been a qualified doctor for only six weeks.

'Do you know the anatomy?'

'Yes.' I decided to be bold.

With that, he handed me the scalpel. 'Good. You are about to do your first one now. Tell me what you are going to do just before you do it and remember the femoral artery is just deep to where you will be operating. For goodness' sake, do not cut that or we'll all be in trouble. Good luck.'

Shaking slightly, I picked up the scalpel and made the incision where Mr Cowie indicated, dissected through the layers while doing my best to name them, defined the hernial sac, excised it and carried out what I later learned is called a Bassini repair to prevent recurrence. I put a neat row of stitches into the skin at the end and applied a dressing.

'What do you want to do career wise?' came the voice over my shoulder.

'General practice, I think.'

'Mike, I think you should do surgery. You have got good hands and you will be a Consultant in ten years,' came the response.

I looked up at the theatre clock and, realising how long I had taken to do the procedure, thanked the anaesthetist for his patience and more or less floated out of the operating theatre and skipped down the stone stairs. Such chance occurrences shape our futures. Mr Cowie might not have been a patient man, I could have dropped the scalpel or answered that I didn't know the anatomy, which frankly would have been more accurate. Or maybe there wouldn't have been enough time on the list to let an HO do a case. In any of those scenarios, I would almost certainly have continued on to become a GP.

I moved to UCH for the latter half of my surgical house job. The set-up there provided a more general surgical experience, and the Registrar, Simon Harries, taught me how to do appendicectomies and varicose vein operations and after theatre or ward round we would frequently go to the Sun to work our way through their impressive offering of unusual beers.

The firm was led by Mr Russell, another eminent Consultant. He was well known as having exacting standards and there would be more than a frisson of anxiety whenever he came to the ward. I was one of four junior doctors on his firm and we would more or less line up when he arrived, forming a sort of guard of honour. His habit was to test our knowledge of the patients by asking us individual blood test results even when it was clear that he already knew the answers. Our policy in response was to allow any one of the four junior doctors on the firm who knew the answer to blurt it out even if they were not the one being quizzed. In this way, we covered each other's backs, even though it clearly frustrated Mr Russell.

* * *

Moving to Bath in early February 1992 for my second house job was like opening a large window to a stuffy room. From the cardiology ward of the Royal United Hospital I could see hills, and it was a joy to be out of central London. The firm was led by my Consultant, Dr Hubbard, with Registrar Tim Edwards and SHO Mike Mullen. Again, I was living on site in hospital accommodation along with all the other HOs, which allowed for regular visits to Bath's pubs and clubs. All of this was making me realise that I was suited to life as a hospital doctor; a prerequisite for anyone even vaguely contemplating becoming a surgeon.

The on calls were less frequent than I was used to in London but they offered ample training opportunities. I had learned at the Middlesex that if you don't push yourself forward you won't learn, and I asked to do some of the procedures that Tim and Mike were doing.

'Okay, you watch me do the next central line insertion and you can do the one after.'

I soon got used to performing that and similar procedures and "graduated" to do lumbar punctures, finding the steady drip of clear spinal fluid coming out of the end of the particularly long needle I had placed into the spinal canal especially rewarding.

Not only was I taking to hospital life but the fact that I was enjoying carrying out procedures made a career in surgery look more and more likely. But lack of sleep combined with mental tiredness from working intensely under high pressure was taking its toll.

During the Sunday afternoon of one particularly busy on-call "weekend" – Friday morning to Monday evening – seeing patient after patient day and night, I was walking from the wards back to my hospital accommodation when I started to hear a buzzing sound. I stopped and searched around me. What on earth was it? I couldn't see an insect but it was loud and intrusive and I frantically waved my arms about to try and get away from whatever it was. The sound continued but then transformed into a high-pitched tinkle as if from a small bell. It followed me all the way back to my room where I collapsed fully clothed on to the bed and fell deeply asleep for some hours. I felt groggy when I was awakened by my phone ringing – my brother – and was alarmed to discover that he had phoned me an hour previously while I was asleep. Apparently, I had answered and we had a brief conversation of sorts but I hadn't been making any sense so he was phoning back to make sure I was okay. I had no recollection of that conversation at all. I was still on call. Had I had other conversations that I couldn't remember where I was talking nonsense? The good news was that the noises that had been troubling me had disappeared and it seemed clear what they had been – auditory hallucinations from lack of sleep.

Despite the hard work, I enjoyed my time at Bath, and it was a sad day in July 1992 when I left in my elderly Ford Fiesta packed with my worldly belongings bound for Basildon to work as a "Casualty officer" for six months. This was a common route following house jobs because it would provide a wide spectrum of clinical experience, with the added benefit of not having to commit to a particular career path. I drove to Orsett Hospital, where my accommodation was based, a few miles from Basildon, and unloaded my stuff into a small room with a single bed. A look round showed a communal bathroom at the end of the corridor. The absence of any kitchen facilities was remedied by the rapid purchase of a microwave oven and tiny fridge, which together seemed to take about half of the available floor space of my room.

Casualty jobs are structured differently – there would be no on call but instead a shift pattern of fifty-six hours per week. There would be an additional night spent in a "bedroom" off a corridor close to the A & E department where we would each (there were eight of us) spend a night in rotation, so that we could help out if it got very busy. In reality, this bedroom was a small storeroom housing various bits of redundant hospital equipment and old dusty filing cabinets. There were no windows, it was hot and noisy, and lying there with a bleep waiting to go off was a miserable experience, compounded by the fact that it was unpaid.

It was a very busy department and, regardless of the time of day, I would walk in to be confronted by a huge queue of patients and an exhausted-looking colleague ready for handover.

'These four are off having X-rays', they would say, indicating a pile of casualty notes. 'These five are in cubicles having obs (observations) done, we are waiting for surgical reviews on these two and there are about fifteen in the waiting room. Oh, and there's one in resus (a clinical area off the side of the Casualty department reserved for resuscitating the sickest patients) and one of the nurses has just taken a blue light message about an RTA on the A27 – three are expected by ambulance inside twenty minutes.'

The unsatisfying reality was that however hard we worked we would never get on top of it, as the patients would just keep coming.

Most of it was fairly trivial stuff – sprained ankles, cut fingers "?fishbone stuck in throat" was surprisingly common, "FB (foreign body) in eye", etc. With the aid of a strong light, some magnifying loupes and some fine forceps, I became adept at removing foreign bodies from various bodily orifices – commonly nostrils and ears (mostly small beads) – but, memorably, from a toddler's ear on one occasion, the remnants of a dead insect. I enjoyed it when there was suturing to do, taking pride in making the stitches as neat as possible; my experience in Jamaica and house jobs serving me well.

I had been in the job for three months when I was roused from poor sleep by my bleep. It was my turn to sleep in the "cupboard", as we called it. It was 2 a.m. on a Sunday morning and sleepily I got dressed and walked round the corner to be confronted by "carnage", as we used to call it – all the cubicles were full, additional patients were in resus and a full waiting room. Saturday night in Basildon had taken its toll.

The colleague who had bleeped me looked stressed. 'I'm sorry to wake you up', she said, 'but I could really do with a hand.'

'Don't worry', I replied. 'What do you want me to do? Looks like a war zone.'

'There's someone in resus I need to attend to and I've sent someone off with constipation for an X-ray. He's coming back now. Perhaps you see him and I'll go to resus?'

'Fine', I said, as the man was being wheeled back into his cubicle.

I read his notes: Mr Ashdown: abdominal pain, constipation. Sent for X-ray. I looked at the X-ray and could just about convince myself of some faecal loading in the colon. I had a chat with him. He was grateful and even apologetic for 'being a nuisance'.

'It looks like constipation to me', I said.

'Thought so', he replied. 'Can you give me something for this dreadful pain?'

It struck me as slightly odd then – as it does now that I write these words – that he was requesting a painkiller for constipation rather than something to help his bowels move, but he had already been examined, a diagnosis made and the X-ray seemed to confirm it. Also, there was the practicality that it was 3 a.m. and there were many other patients to see. I prescribed him some medication – both painkillers and laxatives – discharged him and, after seeing a few more patients, returned to the storeroom to try to resume my sleep.

When I came in later that day for my regular shift there was a distinctly sombre mood among the Casualty staff. And then one of the nurses broke the news to me that, just a few hours after he arrived back home, Mr Ashdown had sadly collapsed and died. Worse was to follow in the next day or two as the local newspaper got hold of the story: "War veteran Alf Ashdown, 68, died just hours after being sent home at 4 a.m. by doctors...."

It transpired that Mr Ashdown had died of a burst abdominal aortic aneurysm. Presumably the aneurysm was the cause of his pain; the fact that he hadn't opened his bowels for a few days was a red herring. Needless to say, I felt dreadful. Why hadn't I examined him myself? After all, it was me who saw him last and who discharged him. I can still to this day see his face in my mind's eye, despite the fact that I met him for only perhaps ten minutes, and I have always felt that I let him down.

I learned a lot from that experience and resolved to do better next time. From now on, I decided, I would be utterly methodical. I would never accept others' findings uncritically but would always make a point of assessing the evidence available myself before coming to a diagnosis. I was still deciding what career to pursue, and there was something about this experience that put me off general practice. Any GP seeing Mr Ashdown in primary care might reasonably have come to the conclusion that he was constipated. How much better it is in a hospital, I thought, that you have at your disposal all the diagnostic tools you could ever need and colleagues to collaborate with.

Pursuing a career in surgery would involve an additional decade or so of further study while continuing to work as a junior doctor, but I knew in my heart of hearts it would be worthwhile. First, I needed to see if I could stomach the huge amounts of academic study that would be required and so started rereading my anatomy textbooks.

I would need plenty of time to study to pass the very tough initial surgery exams on the way to becoming a Fellow of the Royal College of Surgeons (FRCS), so what better way to do it than by teaching anatomy to medical students? I managed to secure a job as an anatomy demonstrator to first-year medical students at Queen Mary College, University of London, helping them with dissections of cadavers, as I had done all those years before. This was a split job combined with working half the week (sixty hours!) as a Resident Medical Officer (RMO) at a BUPA hospital in Brentwood. I packed up the Fiesta, headed for Brentwood and moved into a small room in the hospital.

I was to be resident at the BUPA hospital for two and a half days per week continuously, available for straightforward tasks such as taking bloods and completing drug charts, but would also often be the first called by the nurses for any clinical problems. It was expected that there would be a few hours every day when I could study for my primary FRCS exams and prepare my talks and demonstrations to the medical students towards the end of the week. At times, I even made it into theatre to help with various procedures, and I well remember a Consultant coming out of theatre one evening triumphantly declaring he had just done the hospital's first laparoscopic appendicectomy, declaring with a faraway look in his eyes 'It's the future, you know.'

Requiring some formal tuition to help get me through the primary FRCS exam, I enrolled on the "Slome course". Professor Slome was a legendary teacher to generations of budding surgeons, and it was a real privilege spending six weeks in a lecture theatre at King's College in the Strand being prepared for the primary FRCS. Although eighty-seven years old, he still had tons of energy and was an inspiring teacher.

The course – together with the time I had invested in teaching anatomy and pounding the books – paid off, because, when I took the exam in October 1993, I was among the twenty-five per cent of people who were deemed to have done well enough to pass. The reward was that I would be entitled to study further – for the Part 2 FRCS a couple of years hence! While simultaneously celebrating and contemplating the years of study ahead, I remembered a lecturer at medical school once pausing his talk to ask us who intended to become surgeons. His response to the smattering of hands that went up was that the average age of becoming a Consultant Surgeon was thirty-eight. I was by now twenty-seven and at that moment unsure whether I would have the stamina to keep going as a junior doctor for another eleven years.

I was appointed to the SHO surgical rotation at Northwick Park Hospital to start the following March, but I was now officially broke and so scoured the *British Medical Journal* (BMJ) jobs section for a vacant locum position. I spotted one that might suit: for three months in Leeds on a transplant surgery firm. I was having a vague thought of doing urology, and transplant surgery would be useful because it would expose me to kidney transplants. I was interviewed at "Jimmy's" (St James's University Hospital) and was successful, along with another candidate; the job due to start more or less straightaway.

Arriving late one evening at the nurses' home at Jimmy's, I carried my belongings up the winding staircase into my room on the first floor. The floral wallpaper, elderly utilitarian furniture and dusty smell of hospital accommodation were familiar. I went downstairs to the communal kitchen – dirty pots and pans piled in the sink and the fridge crammed with half full cartons of milk and a smattering of Tupperware boxes containing the remnants of food. Various labels had been stuck to the outside of these items with the names of the owners and various messages: "Hands off!" and "Please leave!"

On meeting the other members of the firm early the next morning, it was clear that transplant surgery was very different from anything I had done before. While I found the surgery fascinating and was comfortable with the daily routine of ward round, clinic and theatre, I didn't take to the unpredictability of the on calls. Nights were commonly disturbed by the transplant coordinator: 'We've got a retrieval. See you at the hospital entrance in ten minutes.' We would then pile into a van and speed to one of a variety of destinations in the north of England.

On arrival at whichever hospital it was, we would change into greens before entering theatre where lay an unfortunate person, brain dead but being kept alive by an anaesthetist. Our job was to take the liver and kidneys but other organs would be simultaneously retrieved by other surgical teams – pancreas, heart and lungs, corneas – and, given that time was of the essence, it was not uncommon to have a number of surgical teams operating side by side. We would all operate as quickly as we reasonably could and then fly off into the night like birds of prey with our respective organs on ice in polystyrene boxes.

Although it was very rewarding seeing people being transformed by receipt of a new liver or kidney, it was clear that transplant surgery was not for me. In order to create as little disruption to the routine lists as possible, many of the operations took place at unsociable hours and, while some thrive on not knowing what the day will bring, I was not one of them, and was relieved to be driving back down the M1 at the end of February the following year to move into a shared flat in Archway to start my SHO rotation.

Northwick Park Hospital is a large and busy District General Hospital (DGH) in north London, and it would be my place of work for the next two years as I rotated through Casualty (again), Orthopaedics, vascular surgery and Urology. I would do a one-in-four rota with internal cover and I was reassured that I would gain some surgical independence by having my own operating lists of minor operations, such as carpal tunnel decompression, knee arthroscopy and cystoscopy.

The work in those years was all consuming with not much time for anything else – the one-in-four on-call rota with internal cover meant one-in-three much of the time. It proved necessary to have an early night before being on call, the night on call usually afforded little sleep, and the night following an on call required hitting the sack early to recover from the lack of sleep the previous night. There were ample training opportunities but it was exhausting work, made a little easier by developing the skill to snatch sleep whenever and wherever I could. I'd sometimes even nap on a spare operating table commonly found in the theatre corridor, with one of the nurses or operating department practitioners (ODPs) waking me as the next patient was being sent for.

Towards the end of the two years, I sat for the FRCS Part 2. This meant attending the RCS for a set of vivas: spoken examinations on anatomy, pathology, surgery and physiology. The top fifty per cent would pass. By late afternoon, all eighty or so candidates had been examined and we assembled as instructed in the foyer of the RCS in Lincolns Inn Fields. The successful candidates were announced in alphabetical order and invited to cross the foyer to pass the statue of John Hunter and enter a large meeting room; a symbolic welcoming into the RCS. Those whose names were not called were left to slope off home.

There were an agonising number of candidates whose surname began with "S": 'Saladin, Samuels, Shah, Shelton… Swinn.' I crossed the foyer, turned left as instructed and was handed a glass of warm white wine.

'Congratulations, well done', a beaming examiner declared. With a huge sense of relief, I had at last become an FRCS. This meant that I was deemed to have a certain amount of academic and surgical knowledge, but in practice meant that I was now deemed to be sufficiently well qualified to apply for training in my chosen speciality, which I was sure by now would be urology.

The next day, a smiling Mr Mee, my urology Consultant at Northwick Park, addressed me. 'Mr Swinn, well done.'

I had now earned the title of "Mr".

I asked about urology training.

'It's very competitive at the moment', he said. 'It has all been Calmanised', he added, referring to recent changes in UK medical training. 'And, as you know, there are many more applicants than places. You could always do general surgery first to give you an edge.'

The suggestion of yet more training before urology training was unappealing to say the least but, in my heart of hearts, I knew that it was sound advice. I went straight to the library to plough through the jobs section of recent copies of the *BMJ* in search of suitable vacant positions.

CHAPTER 3

Registrar and Fellowship years

FOR DECADES, THE NHS TRAINING SYSTEM meant that an aspiring hospital Consultant would work their way up through the ranks from junior doctor all the way up to Senior Registrar level, at which point they could apply for a Consultant post.

The problem was that there were a great many more Senior Registrars than vacant Consultant posts, creating a bottleneck, with many stuck at Senior Registrar level for several years. Some were well into their mid-forties before finally being appointed a Consultant and escaping the ranks of the so-called "junior doctor".

To resolve the situation, Sir Kenneth Calman was tasked in the 1990s with streamlining training so that there would be more formalised competitive entry to Registrar level, with the number of available Registrar posts being roughly matched to the anticipated number of Consultants in future years. Furthermore, Registrar training would be time limited to generally five years.

This meant that the main hurdle to becoming a Consultant had been moved forward to entry at Registrar level, and, while this was sensible, in practice it meant that the bottleneck had merely been brought forward. To this day, more than forty per cent of the total medical workforce in the UK remain in the junior doctor ranks. Bringing the bottleneck forward meant that anyone failing to get appointed on to a training scheme in their chosen speciality within a relatively short period of time ran the risk of becoming time expired and having to face the ignominy of switching careers.

The onus was therefore on me to do as much as I could to be as competitive as possible when applying for Registrar training. The two things I could do to achieve this were general surgery and research, and the best candidates generally did both. Having scoured the BMJ jobs section for a few weeks, I spotted something suitable and, after an interview, started as a "senior SHO" in general surgery in Guildford in spring 1996.

The high property rents in Guildford were unaffordable on a junior doctor's salary and, settling on shared hospital accommodation, I once again unloaded my possessions from the car into a small flat on the hospital campus. I was now used to having a single shared toilet and tiny kitchen, but what was different about this relatively new build was that the walls were so thin that my flatmate's bleep going off in the middle of the night would wake me up too. This would be followed by the sound of him swearing, getting dressed and slamming the door behind him.

By "senior SHO", what they meant was that I would be paid as an SHO but act as a Registrar. I took a full part in the on-call Registrar rota and again had my own lists of relatively minor operations – hernia repairs, and so on, and I would do parts of the bigger operations that the Consultant did. One day I looked at what was coming up on my list later in the week and, among the varicose veins and the like was "above knee amputation". Now, while I was familiar with the concept of "see one, do one, teach one", the problem with me doing this particular operation was that I had never even seen one. This was pre-internet, so I took myself off to the library and dug out a dusty tome called "Operative Surgery" or some such and found a helpful couple of pages with diagrams on how to do the operation – where to make the incision, how to saw through the bone and, importantly, how to leave enough muscle and skin to fold over the cut end of the bone to act as a flap.

The day came and I carefully marked out with a pen where my incision would be. 'Alright if I start?' I asked the anaesthetist casually, trying to sound calm.

'Please do', came the response, and I picked up the scalpel and sliced through the skin and muscle along the pen lines. I cut through a sheaf of nerves and all was going according to plan until I reached some hefty blood vessels. I thought I had clamped them adequately but, as I cut through them, I encountered swift bleeding.

There is little more disconcerting to a surgeon than bleeding of such a velocity that it becomes audible. It makes a sort of sickening whooshing sound and you know when you hear it you're in trouble. The sucker was sucking and the clamps were clamping but the blood kept coming and obscuring my view.

'Is everything alright?' – my kindly anaesthetist.

'Er, no. Not really. Brisk bleeding and I need some help please', I managed to blurt out. Someone was dispatched from theatre and, a long ten minutes later, Liam arrived.

Liam was the Australian Fellow, and I have rarely been happier to see anyone before or since. He quickly scrubbed and, when he joined me, it was clear that he had at least seen the operation before and probably even done one or two because within twenty minutes the bleeding had stopped and the patient was stable. I sawed through the bone and removed the necrotic, ulcerated leg and he left me to finish the flap as he had to go back to his own operating list. I thanked him profusely, and he left with a cheery 'Rightio, mate.'

As a surgeon you have to take risks, and operations are not always comfortable. Sometimes there are parts of them that are scary, but what I had done here was beyond that – I had embarked upon an operation that I was not qualified to do. I berated myself and resolved at that time never again to get myself into that situation. Additionally, I was grateful to Liam for the way in which he conducted himself during the operation – he could have tutted his way through resentfully, but he was magnanimous, even commenting on what an unusually difficult case it was (although I suspect it wasn't), and saying at a volume that everyone could hear how well I had done to get as far as I had. Multiple lessons learned.

The day-time elective lists were usually less stressful than that but perhaps because of the proximity of some major roads or the nearby army camp at Aldershot, there was a significant amount of emergency work out of hours. As the general surgical Registrar on call I felt distinctly uncomfortable, particularly on hearing trauma calls, because it meant that I would have to make my way quickly from the hospital accommodation to Casualty, to be met by the nursing sister handing me a fluorescent yellow vest to wear over my clothes with the words "Trauma Team Leader" emblazoned across the front.

One Saturday night at about 11 p.m. I got such a call, made my way over and donned the vest. 'RTA. Four men, ETA imminent. It's very serious – one dead.' I readied myself and, as they were wheeled in on trollies, was saddened to hear their ages – the oldest was nineteen.

I spoke to the paramedics about what had happened, the state the car was in, how they got the men out. Two were in reasonable shape – the back-seat passengers, I assumed – one was dead and the fourth was screaming loudly. As I walked up to him there was no evidence of the cause of his pain – blood, cuts, broken bones, etc. I could see his neck was in a brace but a quick glance at the monitors showed all his observations to be fine.

I started talking to him but could not be heard due to his screaming, repeatedly asking after his friend, the one who had died.

'Let's concentrate on you for a minute', I said weakly.

'I can't feel anything', he said.

I asked him to move his legs – nothing. His arms – nothing. I stroked the sharp end of a tenson hammer against all four limbs – no sensation. He had suffered a catastrophic neck injury and was paralysed from the neck down. He was not screaming due to pain but rather a visceral, gut-wrenching response to the realisation of the situation he was in and what had happened to his friend.

I found instances like this traumatic and, although many aspects of the elective side of the work appealed, I was not a natural fit to the emergency environment. It confirmed my belief that a speciality such as urology, which is generally associated with less emergency work, would suit me better. So, towards the end of my year at Guildford, I applied for the West London urology specialist Registrar training scheme. Just about ten per cent of those applying would be accepted on to it and I was delighted to be shortlisted.

As I sat in the waiting area on the interview day, I started chatting to one of the other candidates, who seemed lost in his own thoughts.

'Where are you working at the moment?' I asked.

'Me? I'm just doing a painting and decorating job at the moment. My job finished and I couldn't get a decent locum, so, well, it pays the bills.'

I was shocked that a man of about thirty, who had been a qualified doctor for six or seven years, was spending his time like that.

'In fact', he continued, 'if I don't get this job today I'm off. Packing it in. I'm fed up and I've decided to just go and do something else instead.'

As it turned out, he did get one of the jobs on offer, but I didn't. I think it was the first time I had been unsuccessful in a job application, so I couldn't grumble, but it was nonetheless disappointing.

Just as I was reconciling myself to spending another year in general surgery, the next day my phone went.

'Hello, Christopher Woodhouse here. With whom am I speaking please?'

Mr Woodhouse was an eminent London urologist, who had been on the interview panel. He explained that I had done well but it was just that there were others ahead of me in the queue, so to speak. He suggested that I telephone Dr Clare Fowler with a view to discussing the possibility of doing research for a couple of years before joining the scheme.

Dr Fowler was a "uro-neurologist". In other words, a neurologist with an interest in people with bladder symptoms of a neurological cause. In fact, she coined the term. We arranged to meet, struck up an instant rapport and I started at the National Hospital for Neurology and Neurosurgery, Queen Square, London, a couple of months later.

The change from purely clinical practice was welcome and "Queen Square", as the hospital was always referred to, proved to be an endlessly fascinating repository of rare clinical cases. As a tertiary referral centre, it received patients from all over the country, whose cases were usually baffling, or at the very least, extremely rare.

There were two sides to the job: research, which included teaching, writing papers and giving presentations; and clinical.

The clinical side involved seeing patients with bladder symptoms of a neurological cause on the ward or in the outpatient department, and I soon developed an interest in "Fowler's syndrome". Named after my consultant Clare Fowler, this is a rare disorder affecting predominantly young women and characterised by painless urinary retention. We developed a treatment programme for them involving so-called "sacral nerve stimulation". This involved surgically implanting a pacemaker-like device under the skin and connecting it to an electrical lead placed in one of the holes in the back of the sacrum. The electric current modified the activity of the bladder and, for some, it was literally like flicking a switch. Their previously useless bladders, which had been unable to contract at all, suddenly became functionally normal.

I was fascinated how technology could affect bodily function, and there was no doubting the transformation it had in so many aspects of our patients' lives. One lady felt that getting rid of her catheter now permitted her to embark on her first serious relationship, and she later kindly brought in slices of her wedding cake, which we ate in the department with much satisfaction.

The research side led me to meetings all over the world. I love travelling, and this proved a great way to see many places that otherwise I would not have visited. As a urological surgeon in a predominantly neurological environment, I always felt my neurological knowledge inadequate and I would sometimes get nervous before giving a presentation.

Once, I was giving a talk at an international meeting in Jerusalem to hundreds of the world's most eminent neurologists, when, instead of asking for my next slide, I mistakenly asked, 'Could I have my next patient please?' Much laughter followed, and the self-confidence I had been trying to summon in order to sound authoritative evaporated instantly as I shrank behind the lectern.

I was enjoying my time at Queen Square and managed to publish some papers in major scientific journals. Having passed my Masters of Science degree (MSc) in urology, I decided to stay on to study for an MD, a postgraduate research degree awarded for original research carried out in a clinical or health care-related context. I surmised that, having two postgraduate degrees in addition to my BSc degree in the history of medicine I had done while a medical student, as well as my basic medical degree, it would enhance my competitiveness when it came to applying for Consultant jobs.

Towards the end of my research, I was looking forward to getting back to clinical work and, eight years after qualifying as a doctor, and with my MD thesis still needing to be written up, I finally started a five-year training programme in my chosen speciality of urology. I was allocated to Charing Cross Hospital and, having moved into a small rented flat in north London, started there the week of the Paddington rail crash, which resulted in the cancellation of some elective work. When the operating lists restarted, I was particularly struck by one my consultants, the late Tim Christmas, who combined awesome surgical skills with great humour.

He took on all manner of cases judged by others to be largely hopeless, such as massive kidney cancers growing up the vena cava into the chest, and difficult cystectomies (removal of the bladder and surrounding structures). Few surgeons were comfortable to take on such immense surgical challenges that carried with them a high complication rate, including death. But the consequences of not operating on many of these patients was inevitable deterioration, and this tricky balancing act led to a series of difficult, sensitive discussions with patients and their families.

It proved an ideal first Registrar job for me, with a combination of simple surgery on day lists, more complex elective operating on the main operating lists and the very major surgery of Tim Christmas. At the end of the year, I left to go to Hillingdon Hospital for a year, and my Registrar colleague, David Hrouda, went off to Brisbane. This sounded much more attractive but I tucked that thought away.

At Hillingdon, I was given great training by my Consultant, Alvan Pope, who taught me many of the techniques of open cystectomy. This was a long and technically demanding procedure but ultimately very satisfying. There was a lot of travelling and I would arrive home late and tired but managed to start writing up my thesis in the evenings and weekends. Getting back particularly late one night, I decided I needed a change of scene and contacted the Princess Alexandra Hospital in Brisbane requesting a fellowship there two years hence.

The next year at St Mary's Hospital, Paddington, was a busy year generally as I was still writing up my MD thesis. I got married in May to Lesley, a nurse specialist at Queen Square, and passed my FRCS(Urol) exit exam in the October. This was my final professional exam and meant that I was now a qualified urologist. While preparing to move to Australia at the end of the year, I finished my thesis and submitted it to the University of London and waited for a date for my viva.

This took place in November 2002, a few weeks before going to Australia. On the appointed day, I settled into my seat before two examiners, whose task it was to viva me for the next two or three hours and see if I had done sufficient work of high calibre to merit the award of an MD. I knew both examiners well, as one was the internal examiner with whom I had collaborated on a number of projects and the other was a urologist I had met many times at various meetings.

The interrogation went well and, at the end of the afternoon, I was asked to go out while they deliberated, and, when I went back in, one of them said, 'You've done some good work and you presented very well this afternoon ... but I'm afraid there is only one possible outcome – and that is that you have been awarded an outright fail.'

To begin with, I thought it must be a joke but they assured me it wasn't: they were concerned that I had not provided them with evidence of ethics approval for a small part of it and they therefore felt that they had no choice.

I left the building and went across the road to the pub where Clare was waiting for me with the expectation that we would have a celebratory drink. She was very disappointed and upset, but I was more sanguine about it – Lesley was now twenty weeks pregnant and we would soon be swapping London November gloom for sunny Brisbane. I suspect Clare knew that it would all come good, but it would take a lot more time and effort if I was going to be awarded an MD.

A few weeks later, Lesley and I left Heathrow bound for Brisbane via Bangkok and Sydney. Once in the air, we were reminded that it was New Year's Eve as we looked down on the numerous firework displays across Europe. We arrived in Brisbane to beautiful heat, checked into our rented apartment at South Bank late afternoon and went for a walk on what was now a midsummer's evening. Children were swimming and playing catch in the pool beside trees laden with flying foxes, and the bars and restaurants were starting to fill with families celebrating the start of the weekend. The whole atmosphere was relaxed and a world away from London with the recent exam and MD viva experiences.

I learned quickly that Australia's health care and training system was different from the UK's in a number of respects. The first was that as the "Fellow" I would be largely responsible for the running of all the theatre lists whether they had small or big operations on them. 'G'day Swinny, what have you got on your list tomorrow?' was a frequent telephone call that I received from Peter Heathcote, my Consultant. The emphasis may seem subtle but it was implicitly clear to me that these patients were mine. I would be operating on and responsible for them, and I relished the step-up in responsibility.

My timetable was for just one clinic per week and the rest of the time was spent operating in theatre. This was a surgical trainee's dream and I was enjoying my job more than ever and learning surgical skills quickly, particularly the bigger operations, which I found the most satisfying. We would do the major pelvic cancer operations together: Dr Heathcote, left-handed, would do one side, and I, right-handed, would then effectively do the mirror image and try to emulate him as much as possible. He was a great trainer – appropriately supportive when needed but hands-off enough to let me develop my surgical skills. It was no surprise when he was soon after elected president of the Urological Society of Australia and New Zealand.

As a tertiary hospital, the Princess Alexandra received referrals from all over the state and it took me a while to understand the distances involved. One morning, soon after starting, I took a call from a doctor in Windorah wanting to admit a patient with stones blocking his kidneys. The patient certainly needed to come to hospital and I accepted the referral. Late in the day he still hadn't arrived and I mentioned it in passing to a colleague.

'Where's he coming from?'

'Windorah.'

'Windy? That's miles away! Did you book the plane?'

I wasn't sure if he was joking but, sure enough, it turned out that "Windy" was about as far away from Brisbane as Spain from London, and accepting a referral of this nature required a fair bit of logistical organisation.

There was another key difference between Australian practice and that in the UK and for a while I couldn't put my finger on it. But then it slowly dawned on me: there was an absence of targets and a relative absence of managers, perhaps as a consequence, with doctors having a far greater role than in the UK in the running of the hospital. One day I was in the doctors' office by the ward when one of my consultants, Peter MacTaggart, opened his post. Whatever he read, he was clearly aghast.

'Well, will you look at that?', he said out loud. 'What a load of nonsense!', he continued, clearly incredulous at what he was reading. 'There's only one place for that!' And with that he stood up on a chair, pushed up a ceiling tile and posted the letter into the void above, never to be seen again. He replaced the tile, stepped down off the chair and repeatedly brushed his hands together, dislodging imaginary dust or dirt. 'That ought to take care of that.'

'What was that?', I asked.

'Oh, just a stupid letter from some manager or other.'

Back home, Clare had been busy appealing the decision on my MD. Her appeal had secured the right to a hearing at Senate House, the University of London's headquarters. She notified me jubilantly, but the thought of going back to London to be quizzed by the appeal panel did not fill me with enthusiasm. She sensed my reticence, and

Clare very generously offered to stand in for me and I gladly accepted.

The appeal was heard and the conclusion was that I had won the right to resubmit my thesis to a fresh pair of examiners. It would mean having to go through the whole viva process again but I had spent so long on it – and I felt I would be letting Clare down if I didn't – and so agreed. Another set of examiners was duly found with the plan that I would be examined on it the following year.

Our daughter, Olivia, was born uneventfully In February and we moved from the Queenslander we had rented initially into a smart new pad on Kangaroo Point. Those days of endless sunshine, of Lesley swimming daily in the nearby pool in Musgrave Park with baby Olivia in the pram by the side and of me loving my amazing job were some of the most carefree and happy I had ever had. Neither Lesley nor I could have foreseen or even really imagined the stresses that within a couple of years would change all of that.

CHAPTER 4

Becoming a Consultant

DURING THE LATTER HALF OF THE YEAR in Brisbane, with our return home looming, our attention turned to the fact that, soon after arriving back in the UK, my training would be deemed to have been completed and I would be able to apply for a Consultant job. My habit was to visit the hospital library on a weekly basis to access the BMJ as soon as it was issued and flip through the pages to get to the very back to find the jobs section. The internet has now changed the process, but for generations the jobs section of the BMJ was the only way to see a list of vacant posts. Lesley and I had grown accustomed to the extra space and short commute we had enjoyed in Australia, and the prospect of going back to living in London was unattractive, especially with a newborn baby. We still wanted to access London and decided we would try and base ourselves within the M25 periphery.

Consultant jobs come up relatively infrequently, and putting a premium on location narrowed our options considerably. For months, nothing even vaguely suitable was advertised, but then, very close to the end of our time in Brisbane, I spotted a job advertised at the Surrey and Sussex Healthcare NHS Trust (SASH), its main hospital being in Redhill, Surrey. Perfect location, we thought, and I set up an informal visit on our return to the UK.

We made the most of our remaining time abroad by travelling around much of eastern Australia and New Zealand. In Brisbane there were various boat trips down to Surfers Paradise with my two consultants, Peter Heathcote and Peter MacTaggart, in their motor-cruiser. Predictably, I missed all of that when we arrived back in the

UK in January 2004 but what I missed most was not being given the responsibility that I had enjoyed at the Princess Alexandra, and it felt the right time to move up to Consultant. I made a number of informal visits to Redhill and met the two consultants already in post, Mr Paul Miller and Mr Abhay Rane, respectively nine and seven years my senior. Both were likeable, we got on well, and they encouraged me to apply.

At interview there were, I think, six candidates, including the two Consultants who had been in post as locum for that job. I looked around the waiting room at the anxious faces. One leaned towards me and broke the silence: 'Hi. I'm Andrew.' I recognised him and felt a little less confident when he declared himself the son of the retiring urologist! As it turned out, I need not have worried – I was phoned later in the day to congratulate me on getting the job. There were some details to finalise about completing my training officially, but finally I was awarded a Certificate of Completion of Specialist Training (CCST). It had taken thirteen years since qualifying as a doctor but I could now be appointed a Consultant, and I started in October 2004.

I was welcomed on the first day by Jill, my brilliant secretary, who had thoughtfully put a small bunch of flowers on my desk. Everyone in the urology office was very friendly and helpful and I settled in quickly. I was not particularly anxious about the operating lists, although my given day of Friday was not ideal because it meant going in on Saturday mornings to check on the previous day's patients. I enjoyed having junior doctors with me in theatre and was impressed with the skills and experience of the two Associate Specialists, Mr Mushtaq Shuja and Mr Ahmed Mohamed.

It was a busy department, performing a wide variety of urological operations ranging from the most basic – cystoscopy (telescopic examination of the inside of someone's bladder for diagnostic purposes) to major pelvic cancer surgery, and pretty much everything in between. Mr Rane concentrated on kidney surgery and pioneered a laparoscopic (keyhole) operation to remove cancerous kidneys. He also removed large kidney stones percutaneously (i.e. through the skin) using minimally invasive techniques. Mr Miller concentrated on prostatic disease and pioneered an operation to remove benign prostate tissue using a Holmium laser. He also was doing some kidney stones and the most major operations – radical prostatectomy and radical cystectomy.

The lists were going well and I even managed to bring some new surgical procedures to the department, such as urethroplasty (a relatively uncommon operation I had learned in London that helps people with a scarred urethra), and tension-free vaginal tape (TVT) insertion for women with urinary incontinence. It seemed a close-knit, busy but happy department. What I was not looking forward to was the prospect of being on call one-in-three with internal cover; the same frequency at which I had started my career when first qualified.

While most problems could be dealt with over the telephone, there were sometimes very major issues that required prompt senior intervention, and I quickly learned that I could never relax when on call. One night a few weeks after starting I was awakened at 5 a.m. by Ahmed on my mobile:

'Morning. Sorry to bother you but we've got a twenty-two-year-old man who fell off his bike riding back from the pub a few hours ago, found by the roadside and blue-lighted in. His haemoglobin's seven, he's hypotensive (low blood pressure) and tachycardic (fast heart rate) and barely rousable,' he explained.

I paused, desperately trying to wake up.

'Doesn't sound very urological so far,' I replied.

'Oh, sorry. Meant to say we did a CT scan and it shows a haemorrhaging left kidney. The only broken bones are a couple of ribs.'

'Splenic injury?', I asked, knowing that if there was then it would be more suitable for the patient to have a joint procedure with the general surgical team and we could perhaps operate on him together.

'No. All other organs are fine.'

'Can you resuscitate him – blood, fluid and so on?'

'We've done all that but his blood pressure is still in his boots and the CT shows an abdomen full of blood so he's just going to keep bleeding until we stop it.'

This was one of the situations that all urologists dread and my mind cast back to the bleeding kidney Mr Cowie came in to operate on in the middle of the night all those years before.

'Okay. I'm on my way in. Can you get theatres ready?'

'Already done that. See you soon.'

I cleared my head and drove in, running through how I would do the operation. This was a life-threatening situation and I wanted to discuss it with someone. Unfortunately, both my consultant colleagues were away and so I telephoned Mushtaq.

'I'll come and give you a hand if you like,' he said without hesitation.

Needless to say, I was delighted to accept, and before long he joined me in theatre. Still not quite sure exactly what I would find, I made a midline abdominal incision and was confronted by a huge blood clot. Using both hands to scoop it out, four or five large receptacles ("kidney dishes", owing to their gently curved shape) were quickly filled.

To get to the kidney, I dissected the large bowel free of its attachments, moved it towards the centre to expose the duodenum and, when I got to the kidney, found it to be lacerated and torn off its artery, which was spurting. We just about managed to access it, and after a few attempts successfully slid the tips of a surgical clamp across it, and with that the bleeding stopped. The case reminded me in many ways of the patient I had been involved with as an HO, although here there was no prospect at all of saving the kidney. Again, given his youth, the patient bounced back quickly and was home within days. Cases such as this are mercifully rare and news of it quickly spread round the hospital.

'Heard about your case the other day', one of the senior general surgeons said one day while passing me in theatres. 'Well done. Not easy that. A difficult operation and you've only been here a few weeks!'

I replied that Mushtaq had been instrumental and I was well aware how fortunate it was that it had gone well, since first impressions last.

On starting the job, I anticipated that I would be comfortable with the operating lists, but a pleasant surprise was how enjoyable I was finding the outpatient clinics. Although generally overbooked, they served as a repository of fascinating people, including many ex-soldiers. Military history has always been an interest of mine and, aware that first-hand accounts of World War II were sadly becoming rarer, I made it my business to ask about their past, and all seemed happy to talk openly about their experiences.

It was humbling to hear what they had been through, and it was both fascinating and a privilege to hear how war had moulded their philosophy of life. Lloyd, a retired GP, put his laid-back approach down to his experience of sprinting, scared witless, up one of the Normandy beaches on D-day, with many of his friends tragically being shot in the process. As a young Spitfire pilot in the Battle of Britain in 1940, Tony described chasing a German fighter plane over the Kent countryside and out to sea. Both planes headed north and Tony eventually ran out of fuel and had to ditch in the sea some-where off the Norfolk coast.

Wilfred described being caught in close-range gunfire at the Battle of Montecasino where he took a bullet to the shoulder. He somehow managed to pull himself along the ground to seek cover but before long was so close to an enemy gun emplacement that he could hear the voices of German soldiers. Knowing he would bleed to death if he didn't get help, he decided he must 'summon up my best schoolboy German', calling out 'Hilf mir bitte!' After a few repeats, he heard a 'Shh', then some muttering before a German soldier emerged from their emplacement and pulled him along by his ankles. An intense discussion took place between the four or five German soldiers, incomprehensible to Wilf, but, contrary to his conviction that he would now be shot, they shuttled him further back behind the line until he arrived at a makeshift hospital. A German medic appeared over him, tore off Wilf's clothes and was about to plunge a scalpel into his shoulder and upper chest when he noticed his stripes. 'Ah, ein Offizier,' he said and with that disappeared and came back a while later with a vial of anaesthetic and a smile on his face – much to Wilfred's relief. After finding his way back to the

Allied lines, he was soon flown back to England for recuperation but just ten weeks later was back on the front line. I found such stories utterly mesmerising.

With hectic clinics, over-full operating lists and a steady flow of emergencies, including the odd very serious on-call emergency, I quickly became busy. Once leave had been taken into account, each of the three of us was on call almost every other day and every other weekend. My two colleagues were equally busy, and Mr Miller had the added burden of doing both radical prostatectomy and radical cystectomy for all suitable patients in the department. Both of these pelvic operations are carried out for cancer and involve complete removal of the relevant organ. These days, both are commonly done by laparoscopic, or "keyhole", surgery, usually with the aid of a robot, but in those days it represented a more major surgical challenge. Prostatectomy involves complete removal of the prostate by disconnecting the bladder from the urethra: the tube through which urine exits the bladder. Cystectomy involves surgical removal, not just of the bladder but also the prostate in a man, and bladder together with uterus, Fallopian tubes and part of the vagina in a woman. In both sexes, the lymph nodes, or glands, in the pelvis are also removed. Once the bladder has been removed, bowel tissue is used either to make a new bladder on the inside of the body or, more commonly, as a conduit to divert the urine away from the pelvis into a bag stuck to the skin on the outside of the abdomen.

A few months after I started, SASH came under pressure to stop doing both these types of major pelvic cancer surgery following the recent "Improving Outcomes Guidance". This was an edict from the Department of Health designed to centralise the provision of cancer services. The plan was for the country to be divided into regions, called "cancer networks", with each one having one Trust, a so-called "cancer centre" doing these cases with the other Trusts in the region – "cancer units" – referring them in to the cancer centre. SASH was in a network of five hospital Trusts in Surrey, Sussex and parts of Hampshire, and there was debate about which Trust would be the new cancer centre. Nobody in the department or SASH management wanted to lose these cases and one thing which worked against us keeping them was that we had only one surgeon performing them. We therefore agreed that I would also do them, although concentrating on cystectomies, with Mr Miller handling the radical prostatectomies.

The new cancer centres would have a further function, which would be to ratify the clinical decisions about cancer management made in the cancer units. A key strand to the change in approach to the management of cancer cases in the NHS in the early years of this century was the advent of the multidisciplinary team (MDT). It had been recognised that the approach to cancer management was complex, that it involved input from nurses and doctors from different specialities, including urology, pathology, radiology and oncology, and that there were regional differences in decision making. The idea was that members of the MDT would meet weekly to discuss each patient with a newly diagnosed cancer and, by applying the cancer management guidelines, would discuss and agree a management plan.

The outcomes of the weekly MDT meetings would be recorded so that the doctors and nurses subsequently seeing the patients in clinic would know what management plan had been agreed. The recording of outcomes would also allow for a degree of oversight, locally at a hospital level, regionally at a cancer network level, and nationally. When I started at Redhill, the local MDT meetings seemed to function adequately and, in time, new cancer diagnoses of prostate, bladder, kidney and testis were further discussed at a regional MDT by those at the cancer centre, referred to as a specialist MDT (sMDT).

I was busy clinically but coping well with the workload and, keen to establish myself more generally in the hospital, made myself available to help with various projects whenever volunteers were sought. In this way, I started attending commissioning meetings with GP leaders, often accompanying the hospital's most senior managers to help lend a clinical perspective and ensure good relationships between the urology department and primary care.

All was going well, but the cloud on the horizon was the prospect of my MD thesis viva. It had now been two years since my original viva and in that time I had spent a year in Australia, moved house four times, had two children (Gemma came along two years after Olivia) and started a Consultant job. The world of Fowler's syndrome and sacral neuromodulation had moved on – as I felt I had – and, if I was going to be awarded my MD, it would require a great deal of time and effort getting up to date with all the papers that had been written in the interim period since my first viva. I was sorely tempted to let it slide but felt that I would be letting down not just myself but those who had helped me get this far. And so, after much time spent getting up to date with the literature, I attended my viva at Senate House at the University of London early in 2005.

Two academic urologists quizzed me for two and a half hours, and when I was called back after a break this time their reaction was very different. "We don't know what the background history of this work is but as far as we are concerned it's very good." There was some minor rewriting to do of one section, which was quickly achieved, and I was soon afterwards delighted to be awarded my MD.

One morning eighteen months after starting as a Consultant, I arrived at my office to go through my post before clinic. I took a moment to reflect on what I had achieved. I had settled into the department, acquitted myself well clinically and had engaged with the wider hospital – even representing it at a high level by accompanying the most senior doctor in the Trust – the Medical Director – at meetings with Commissioners. I opened the first envelope and was amazed to see a letter from the Medical Director asking me if I would like to apply to be Head of the Department of Urology.

'They're sacking me,' Mr Miller said to me later that day with some amusement, walking into my office showing me his letter from the Medical Director saying that his term as Lead had come to an end – and, although he was entitled to apply to retain his role, he should please accept the Medical Director's thanks for doing it these last few years.

I was uneasy at first because Mr Miller had been an effective Lead for quite some time, but he was supportive, as was Abhay, and after a fairly cursory interview by the Medical Director, I started as Head of Department, also known as Clinical Lead, in 2006.

Had I known then what would unfold over the next five and a half years I would have run in the opposite direction as far and as fast as I could.

PART 2
Raising Concerns

CHAPTER 1

2006- 2008

THE FIRST EIGHTEEN MONTHS in my new role were, in retrospect, a honeymoon period. It proved to be a friendly department with good relationships between doctors, nurses and secretaries reinforced by regular trips to a variety of local restaurants. Our son, Henry, came along in 2006 and all was going swimmingly. Unfortunately, an issue would come along soon after I became Clinical Lead that would dominate the agenda and simply could not be ignored.

In the early 2000s, a new treatment for prostate cancer using high intensity focused ultrasound (HIFU) emerged. This was an interesting and potentially useful new way of treating some types of prostate cancer, subject to clinical trials. Mr Miller was naturally drawn to new technologies and often an early adopter. He was a keen proponent of using a Holmium laser to remove benign prostate tissue and introduced the technique of laser enucleation of the prostate to the hospital. To facilitate this, the hospital had for many years rented in lasers from a company owned by Mr Miller for his use. Given his interest in prostate cancer, it was unsurprising that he acquired a HIFU machine and formed a new company that rented it to hospitals, including the local private hospital where he worked.

On hearing this, I was concerned about a possible conflict of interest because, on stepping down as Clinical Lead, Mr Miller had become Cancer Lead for urology. This meant that he would now be responsible for the diagnostic pathways of all patients referred to the department with a potential cancer diagnosis and for the pathways of those diagnosed with cancer. He would also be chairing the MDT meetings. It was clearly of paramount importance that discussions regarding the management options for men with prostate cancer would remain unbiased, and the fact that he owned a company involved with prostate cancer treatment risked compromising that basic requirement. Additionally, the fact that Mr Miller would now chair the meetings might make challenging clinical decisions more difficult.

Unfortunately, within weeks, my worst fears were confirmed. A rose-tinted view of HIFU was presented at MDT meetings, with it being advocated for many patients with prostate cancer. Alongside this, a distorted view of the shortcomings of the three standard management options for men with localised prostate cancer – radical prostatectomy, radiation treatment (from inside or outside the body) and active surveillance – was advanced. The resultant bias towards HIFU was very troubling to many of the MDT members, some of whom expressed their concerns to me.

Initially, I was hopeful that the problem could be resolved by rational discussion and debate, but, as the weeks went by, opposing voices to HIFU were increasingly shut down. Any challenge to decision making was resented and, if anything, served to harden Mr Miller's stance, with his anger frequently directed at those of us who were merely following the guidelines and wishing to steer patients towards more established and appropriate treatments. Looks of bemusement or even horror were exchanged principally between the Oncologist, Abhay, and myself whenever a patient would be directed towards what seemed to us wholly inappropriate treatment.

That the MDT had been subverted in this way was clearly a major clinical safety issue that placed patients directly in harm's way. Not only were their cancer treatments not being discussed in an open, impartial and considered way but the formerly happy, friendly, respectful atmosphere had been replaced by its antithesis, which in turn posed a problem for effective working relationships and patient care.

The two new cancer Clinical Nurse Specialists (CNSs), Kate and Catherine, were particularly concerned and looked to me, as Clinical Lead, to resolve the situation. My initial approach of hoping to achieve balance through rational discussion and debate of the merits of the different treatment modalities had, if anything, seemed to make the situation worse. I was acutely aware of the significant risk to patients' health and well-being and, having been unable to sort it out at a departmental level, decided I had to escalate the issue.

I therefore went to see my manager, the Chief of Surgery, and first saw him in his office one Thursday morning about six weeks after the difficulties had started. I carefully explained to him what was happening, emphasising that concerns were widespread in the department and that it was becoming increasingly difficult for the MDT to function.

I told him: "We are very worried as patients are not getting a good deal. Their treatment plans are being distorted and it needs to stop as some of them will do badly."

He looked at me a little uncertainly. Unusually for someone in that role, he was not a doctor and I wondered whether his lack of medical training might be a hindrance. He was also a direct contemporary of Mr Miller's; they had been colleagues for many years and I wondered if the fact that I had started just eighteen months or so before might make him unsure or even wary of me in some way. I explained and elaborated further, and after a while he said he would look into it.

I assured the CNSs later that day that it was being looked into, and they were very relieved. Unfortunately, in the days that followed, two things were clear: first, that Mr Miller had become angry and uncommunicative – presumably a sign that the Chief had passed on our concerns – and second, he seemed more determined than ever to push his agenda regardless of the unanimous opposition in the MDT.

Kate and Catherine, whose roles included attending cancer clinics with Consultants to help discuss and plan treatments for patients with new diagnoses, were increasingly concerned that the standard treatment options would be dismissed quickly, or sometimes not even mentioned at all. They were also perturbed that patients were being encouraged to arrange HIFU privately, and were not routinely informed that HIFU was available within our network of NHS hospitals. Furthermore, they described occasions when they had been shunted out of the consultation room so they would be unaware of what was said.

This was clearly a serious set of problems, at the heart of which lay the fact that patients were being given suboptimal treatment for their cancers, which I felt might lead to their premature death. I decided to give the Chief some time but, when it became clear that practice hadn't changed after four weeks, I went back to see him.

As I entered his office, he said that he had '…told Mr Miller that you had complained about him' and that he had become angry.

I was dismayed that he had framed it in those terms and responded that I was not so much complaining about my Consultant colleague as raising concerns about patient safety.

'In fact,' I said, 'it is my duty as Clinical Lead to pass on to you concerns that have been expressed to me by the majority of the urology department, doctors and nurses alike.'

The last thing I wanted was for this to be seen as a personal matter, but the way in which it appeared to have been presented to Mr Miller suggested that it had been interpreted as such. That could be potentially disastrous for working relationships within the department and I concluded that Mr Miller's current behaviour was an early, direct consequence. I reassured the Chief that it was nothing to do with personal relationships and I repeated the clinical concerns many of us had about patient management, emphasising that lives were at stake. With that, a serious look came across his face and he again said that he would look into it. Relieved, I fed that back to my colleagues.

Over the next six weeks, the acrimonious discussions in MDT abated but only because HIFU stopped being mentioned. Unfortunately, regardless of what had been decided at MDT meetings, the practice of advocating HIFU in clinic continued. In other words, the MDT had essentially been sidelined. I went back to see the Chief again, and this time was dismayed because it seemed as if he was fed up of talking to me about it.

'Too much politics,' he said with a laugh, completely missing the gravity of the situation where the MDT had been made impotent in challenging an individual doctor who was advocating a new treatment for prostate cancer contrary to guidelines, and in which he had a financial interest.

I reasoned with him again, patiently taking him through why I and so many of my nursing and medical colleagues had concerns over what was going on and the unacceptable care many patients were getting. Reminding him that I was acting in my capacity as Clinical Lead to raise not just my concerns but also those of others in the department, by the end of the conversation he seemed persuaded.

Around this time, I started to be treated differently by some of my Consultant colleagues from other specialities. It was difficult to put my finger on, but I seemed to receive disparaging looks in the corridor. A couple of colleagues with whom I was formerly on very good, friendly terms, became distant and on occasions distinctly unfriendly. I shrugged it off – most of the colleagues falling into this category were contemporaries of Mr Miller, who I guessed had been recipients of a distorted version of events.

One afternoon, I bumped into the Chairman of the Trust's Consultants' Medical Staff Committee. He asked, 'What the hell's going on?'

I explained why I was raising concerns, adding, 'Take it from me, if it was your father with prostate cancer being discussed at our MDT at the moment, you would be pleased I am.'

'Well, you need to be careful. He's phoned up a number of our colleagues telling them what you have done. You can't be a Consultant for twenty years in the same hospital without building up a large set of friends.'

This was unpleasant and unnerving to hear, but I knew in my heart of hearts that I was doing the right thing and, in fact, I had no option but to escalate the issue in the way I had. I went back to see the Chief a number of times – perhaps having a further five or six conversations with him over the next few months in his theatre on some Friday afternoons and in his office on Thursday mornings. I kept him updated, reiterated the concerns of the department and was keen to check on progress. Although perhaps a little vague, he was generally reassuring that something was happening behind the scenes.

But the problems still existed and I protested strongly in one of these visits towards the end of the year that the Trust didn't seem to be doing anything. To this he replied rather unexpectedly that the Trust was looking to dismiss Mr Miller. It was surprising that they would go from doing seemingly nothing about the matter straight to dismissal but I surmised that it was a matter for them, and I was grateful that at last they appeared to be acting. The Chief's view was that it would be difficult to dismiss him on clinical grounds and therefore the Trust would dismiss him on conduct grounds.

'Even if he sues us for wrongful dismissal and we lose, the pay-out is capped at about 70,000 pounds. Cheap at the price,' he told me. And I believed that action was imminent.

Unfortunately, as more weeks and months went by, nothing discernible happened and patients continued to be directed on to unorthodox treatment pathways. I wondered whether the Chief's inaction might be because he had difficulty believing me – or at least in taking me seriously – and so when I next went to see him I took my Consultant colleague Mr Rane with me to demonstrate that I was not a lone voice. Abhay eloquently repeated all the concerns to him exactly as I had done on multiple occasions previously, and I felt that this would surely dispel any lingering doubts the Chief might have had.

I fed back the details of the meeting to the nurses, who by now had reported their concerns separately up through the nursing hierarchy, and sat in my office summarising in my mind where we were. With concerns now being raised by both doctors and nurses up through line management routes, I was now confident it would be just a matter of time before someone would put a stop to it all. We could then do some sort of review to see exactly what had happened to the patients, as we envisaged many would have to be recalled to discuss switching treatments.

A consequence of large numbers of patients with prostate cancer being diverted towards HIFU was a corresponding reduction in the number of patients undergoing conventional treatment, including radical prostatectomy. This significant change in practice started in 2006 and became more obvious to all in the department as time went on. In fact, there were few, if any, patients undergoing radical prostatectomy during the first half of 2007. This was picked up at a national level and, in August 2007, the Director of the National Cancer Action Team wrote to the cancer network Director, copied to the Trust senior management, expressing its concerns. The letter emphasised that HIFU was still experimental and "should only be performed in a setting where more conventional or proven procedures are offered". The letter went on to say that the numbers of radical prostatectomies at the Trust "had fallen to unacceptably low levels and should be transferred out to other, higher volume centres".

A hospital Trust being instructed by a national body in this way was very unusual and, had the Trust focused on what lay behind the abrupt change in practice, the National Cancer Action Team's intervention might have proved to be pivotal. Unfortunately, in the event, nothing changed and cancer patients were still not being offered balanced advice regarding treatment options.

I became disheartened with the lack of progress with the Chief and decided that I must try other routes. SASH had by then created a role known as Cancer Lead, a practising Consultant appointed to take on the additional management role of overseeing cancer management generally within the Trust. Although he was not, strictly speaking, in the management line above me, he nevertheless had responsibility to ensure the quality of cancer delivery, and I thought that he would be the next most appropriate person to hear our concerns. I soon met up with him and, although it was informally over lunch in the hospital canteen, I nevertheless spelled out precisely why I and my colleagues were so concerned.

In the days that followed, I wondered whether I had made an error in broaching a subject as important as this over lunch. In common with other clinical managers, he was carrying out his role of Cancer Lead in addition to a full set of clinical responsibilities, and I was not convinced he would give it the priority it warranted. I therefore decided I should also approach a non-clinical hospital manager.

I thought that the most appropriate person would be the Trust's Director of Operations and, accordingly, I met her in her office in the

Trust's management headquarters. She took on board everything I said, appeared sympathetic and troubled and seemed keen to help. Records show (though not known by me at the time) that she raised the issue with the Chief Executive on two occasions in 2008. Despite this, nothing discernible happened and aberrant practice continued with its associated risk of harm to patients newly diagnosed with prostate cancer and ongoing risk of harm, including premature death, to the growing numbers of those already being managed suboptimally.

Next there was a potentially dangerous turn of events in 2008 when Mr Miller submitted a business case to the hospital for it to rent in his HIFU machine. The Urology Service Manager asked my opinion and, while knowing that opposing it might make for worse relationships in the department, I replied that it would be disastrous, as ready access to HIFU on site would likely result in even greater numbers of patients having it. While the hospital management mulled over the merits of the business case, HIFU was pushed ever more aggressively and, in July 2008, the CNSs wrote to the most senior doctor in the Trust, the Medical Director, regarding the ongoing unsafe clinical environment for patients.

Later the same month, I was asked to give a presentation to the Trust's senior managers, including the Medical Director and the CEO, regarding the urology department's future plans. Occasionally, Trust managers arranged such meetings off site in the hope that it would give "breathing space" to those taking part, and this particular meeting took place at the Reigate Manor Hotel. I duly prepared my talk on the standard topics but included a section on safety and what I considered to be the obvious problems associated with the Trust paying money to a private company owned by a Consultant to facilitate that same Consultant to treat patients. I emphasised the potential for clinical decision making to be distorted. They both nodded their apparent understanding of the issues but did not comment.

Driving home after the meeting, I wondered why they had not reacted more and just hoped that they had understood the issues. Either way, I was pleased that I had now raised concerns all the way up to and including the Medical Director and the CEO. Two weeks later, I met up with the CEO regarding a different issue but used the occasion to clearly tell her of the difficulties we were having and to make sure that she had understood what I had said at the meeting at the hotel.

She again seemed to understand but did not commit to act, and HIFU continued to be pushed, with many patients opting to transfer to the private sector, believing this to be in their best interests. Some had come to believe that HIFU was their only good option for cancer treatment and were even encouraged to approach hospital managers directly to ask them to approve the business case for HIFU. One man was told in clinic that he needed HIFU but that the hospital wouldn't pay for it and, in August and September 2008, he made multiple approaches to the hospital management, literally repeatedly banging on the managers' doors.

This case was discussed at one of the regular monthly cancer meetings chaired by the cancer lead on 15 September 2008. Questions were asked about the patient's management, including why it had been delayed and why the patient had been advised to contact hospital managers directly. The Cancer Lead insisted that the patient be referred to another hospital for treatment and, when he eventually saw the urologist there, it was felt that HIFU would not be an appropriate treatment and the patient underwent a radical prostatectomy.

In retrospect, I believe this incident helped focus the hospital's mind and the business case for renting in HIFU was rejected. With the Trust's rejection, relationships in the department became more strained. The two CNSs, Kate and Catherine, often discussed their concerns with me in my office, as did our Training Registrar. The two Associate Specialists also raised their concerns with me that they were coming across more patients in peripheral clinics, i.e. clinics held in satellite hospitals, who had been promised HIFU once the business case had been approved. Worryingly, some of these appeared not to have received any treatment at all and the specialists described them as being "in limbo".

Abhay was equally concerned about the situation and also repeatedly raised concerns with the Chief of Surgery. One meeting
with him in summer 2008 left him feeling particularly aggrieved. He
went to see the Chief in his office and trotted out the usual concerns
but, on this occasion, instead of being listened to, was told that he
would have to make a formal complaint in writing. Ironically, of
course, going to the Chief of Surgery to express his concerns about
patient management was exactly what he should be doing: the raising
of concerns explicitly does not need to be put in writing; even less
does it have to be a formal complaint.

In addition to writing to the Medical Director, the nurses continued to report their concerns through the nursing hierarchy. Given the
lack of discernible progress, they decided to broaden their approach
and, in August 2008, reported concerns regarding bias towards HIFU
to the Lead Cancer Nurse for the Trust. Again, concerns seemed to
be noted but no action followed.

In fact, rather than matters improving, there was a serious new
concern for us to contend with, and which was raised to the
management: we became aware that a list of potential candidates for
HIFU was being kept and, instead of being offered the treatment as
advised by the MDT, they either received no treatment at all or were
put on a daily tablet of Bicalutamide – a hormone commonly
associated with significant side effects – that might help delay
progression of disease but was not a definitive treatment and offered
no prospect of a cure. The comments from the two Associate
Specialists about coming across patients in limbo with no appropriate
treatment now made more sense.

As is the case in all NHS Trusts, the treatment pathways of all
cancer patients are tracked to ensure that treatment occurs within an
appropriate time frame and according to targets. On starting
Bicalutamide, the clock would stop and they would slip off the
trackers' radar. In other words, not only had these patients been
given the wrong treatment, and one associated with often harmful
side effects, they were in danger of being lost in the system.

I went back to see the Chief yet again, who on this occasion
seemed keen to tell me he was acting Medical Director. This time, I

was aware that my voice was cracking with emotion when I ran through the list of issues. I said that things were getting worse and that the hospital needed to take action without further delay as lives were at stake. He asked me what I thought should happen. I responded that Mr Miller should be suspended to allow an investigation to be carried out. 'At least that way we can stop more patients being harmed and we can sort out some kind of review to get patients onto the right treatment path.'

The Chief responded that the hospital might be better off sacking him. 'Even if we lose the employment tribunal, the compensation we would have to pay him is capped at something like 70,000 pounds,' he again said, unaware that he had told me that before. 'Cheap at the price,' he continued, smiling.

The smiling was difficult to work out. I wondered if he knew something I didn't but was not allowed, perhaps for HR reasons, to let on. What was clear is that I was by now struggling personally. Some of my Consultant colleagues and managers continued to treat me with a sort of suspicious disregard, making my time at work stressful and unhappy. My sleep became erratic at best with the burden of having to sort out the significant issue of patient safety routinely troubling me in the small hours. I had for many months found it difficult to concentrate fully on my work and thoughts of this issue had started seeping into my holidays.

Still, despite my inexperience in issues such as this, I reassured myself that I had done the right thing in escalating concerns to my line manager and also the most senior managers in the Trust. I consoled myself that, in the most recent meeting, I seemed finally to have got through to the Chief and felt that management action was just around the corner.

I could not have known it then but any sliver of optimism was entirely misplaced because matters in all respects were destined to get a whole lot worse.

CHAPTER 2

2009- 2010

IN EARLY 2009, the number of radical prostatectomies at SASH reduced further and, on 22 May 2009, the Trust's Director of Operations emailed the Cancer Lead regarding the need for the Trust to stop doing them altogether due to insufficient volume of cases. When Mr Miller was approached, his response was that he was in fact doing enough and that the appearance that he wasn't was due to a coding issue in the hospital. This assertion went unchecked and he was allowed to continue.

However, since we were not taking a proper part in the cancer network's specialist MDT at Guildford, there was a lack of regional oversight of clinical decision making for prostate cancer patients at SASH. The Cancer Lead realised this and emailed the Chief Nurse in November 2009 raising concerns about the Trust's decision to allow the radical prostatectomy service at SASH to continue and, later that month, met the CEO to discuss his concerns. This finally resulted in radical prostatectomies stopping at the Trust with an instruction that any suitable patients for this surgery be referred out.

Unfortunately, instead of patients being referred via agreed, commissioned pathways, Mr Miller developed the practice in 2009 of referring patients out of area to a variety of hospitals that we had no direct links to. This posed a problem on three fronts: first, it meant that patients, often inconvenienced by having to travel long distances, experienced delays to their treatment; second, the unpredictability, volume and nature of this practice made it almost impossible for the Trust's cancer tracking team to do their job; and finally, it was a disruptive practice, which further undermined the integrity of the MDT itself. This was yet another concern that the urology CNSs and urology Lead Nurse raised with the CEO in January 2009 at which they also reiterated their longstanding background concerns.

Perhaps as a consequence of the cessation of the radical prostatectomy service, enthusiasm for HIFU seemed galvanised and patients continued not to be offered conventional treatments. The continued practice of a Senior Consultant ignoring his medical and nursing colleagues, managers and published guidelines on the management of prostate cancers was clearly putting lives at risk. The fact that he was able to do so more easily by dint of being urology Cancer Lead made it more difficult to challenge this behaviour from within the department, and the practice of farming patients out to a variety of different hospitals in the south-east of England with which we had no links added an extra layer of complexity and difficulty. I had heard nothing more from my line manager, the Chief of Surgery, and decided that I must arrange another meeting with the Trust's Cancer Lead.

This time, we met at a dedicated, formal meeting in his office and I went through all of the concerns one by one. He was receptive to what I was saying and keen to help sort it out. Sighing deeply, he said, 'Okay, I will inform the Medical Director and we need to put something in writing.'

Sure enough, following the meeting, we exchanged emails on 29 January 2010 regarding HIFU being advocated by Mr Miller while not being National Institute for Health and Care Excellence (NICE) approved and the concerns many had regarding it being carried out in the private sector. This culminated in the Cancer Lead emailing Mr Miller on 18 February 2010 requesting that he complied with NICE guidance and not to refer to HIFU as the only treatment option, and, in March, he wrote to the Medical Director about concerns regarding HIFU promotion and Mr Miller's non-compliance with MDT decisions. He made the point that the same concerns had also been raised by the two cancer nurse specialists and the urology Lead Nurse.

We sensed that progress was finally being made and, while this was welcome, I and others remained concerned about the patients already on the wrong treatment pathways. I went to see the Medical Director to reiterate the fact that patients were at risk of harm and pointed out how long it had been going on for. She asked me what I thought should be done and I replied that there should be an external review. She agreed with the suggestion and asked me who I thought could do it. I mentioned a few names, which she wrote down, and I left her office feeling optimistic.

At the following week's MDT, a longstanding patient of the department, 'patient A', was discussed. He had been under regular outpatient review and had now developed metastatic disease, meaning that his prostate cancer had spread. Now that it was present in his bones, the disease would sadly not be curable. The consultant oncologist arranged to see the patient urgently and, when told the diagnosis, the patient was understandably shocked. He pointed out he had been under the care of the department for years with prostate cancer confined to the prostate and was, in fact, waiting for treatment. The patient and oncologist went through everything together from diagnosis to this point and it was clear that, in contrast to the MDT recommendation of radiotherapy, he had been offered only HIFU and was waiting for the hospital to rent in the machine to "zap" the prostate.

Patient A made an official complaint.

Realising the significance of the issue, the Trust categorised it, on 1 March 2010, a serious untoward incident (SUI). This is the most serious category of incident and meant that it would be thoroughly investigated by a senior manager. The opening meeting of the SUI took place on 24 March 2010 with the Medical Director, Head of Integrated Governance, Chief of Surgery and an HR representative all present.

Meanwhile, following my meeting with the Cancer Lead, on 6 April 2010, the Medical Director wrote to Mr Miller, copying in the Chief of Surgery and Cancer Lead, stating that 'A number of serious concerns have been raised about your practice'. I was uneasy at the wording. As far as I was concerned, I had raised concerns about patient safety. The wording made it sound more personally directed at Mr Miller and there was a real danger that relationships in the department would deteriorate further. The letter went on to detail the several areas of concern that I had highlighted to the Cancer Lead. It stipulated that from now on he had to comply with NICE guidelines, could not encourage patients to consult him privately, that he had to involve an oncologist in his decision making and had to have a nurse present in clinic when giving cancer diagnoses and counselling patients regarding treatment options. I read the letter carefully and was pleased that it at least covered all of the areas of concern that I and my colleagues had. It also said, 'We have decided not to suspend your practice at this stage….' with the clear implication that it would do if he did not comply with the stipulations.

With the prospect of an external review, as promised by the Medical Director, as well as the SUI regarding patient A, we were now confident that common sense would prevail and that the whole issue would soon be addressed. I had discussed with the Medical Director the importance and value of having an independent, external expert carry out the review and we had talked about suitable people. I was therefore very disappointed to learn that she had instead decided on an internal review. Moreover, instead of pursuing the two strands of investigation separately, on 9 April 2010, the Medical Director asked Dr Lamb, one of the anaesthetists in the hospital, to conduct an investigation into the allegations of poor practice and to "tie in" the SUI of patient A. This was far from the external review we had been promised; an investigation by someone within the hospital would generally carry far less weight than someone external.

Other concerns were that Dr Lamb was not an expert on prostate cancer and had worked closely with Mr Miller for many years. Never mind, we thought, it's got to be better than nothing, and at least an external opinion was to be sought on the appropriateness of HIFU for patient A. We also reassured ourselves with the knowledge that at least some people within the department would be interviewed as part of the process and would provide an opportunity to state exactly what our concerns were.

With interviews in the offing, many of us wondered how we might be protected from any fallout. It was likely to be disastrous for relationships within the department, but presumably our anonymity would be protected at least to a degree, or at the very least the precise details of who was saying what. The CNSs raised their concerns regarding this issue with the Cancer Lead Nurse and with the surgery division's Chief Nurse and, rather unsatisfactorily, were merely reassured that that Dr Lamb would address their concerns in the review itself.

Finally, a date came through for my interview. On 24 May 2010, as I entered the room, I was shown a seat. Dr Lamb and the Head of Directorate Risk and Patient Safety sat opposite me. Between us on the table were a microphone and a recording device. I looked at them uneasily and gestured towards them.

'Oh, don't worry about that. It's just so we get everything you say down accurately. We will send you a transcript to sign so that you are happy with what you have said.'

I started by stating my reservations about Dr Lamb being the right person to conduct the investigation and suggested that someone external to the hospital with expertise in prostate cancer would be preferable. Having got that off my chest, I answered all the questions as well as I could. When I read the transcript a few days later, I was pleased that I had made my points clearly and unambiguously.

I described the adversarial nature of MDTs and stated: 'It has become clear that several patients have ended up having HIFU when this was not even mentioned at the MDT and sadly at least the ones that have been discussed back in MDT seem to have done badly.'

When asked to elaborate, I continued: 'Some men have been given HIFU in contradiction to the MDT decision and now have recurrent local or metastatic spread.'

I went on to explain that, bizarrely, the solution to men with recurrent disease was to offer them more HIFU rather than switch on to one of the conventional treatment options they should have had previously. I detailed many of the times I had raised my concerns with a variety of senior managers within the Trust, and concluded by stating: 'I still hold the view that there should be some sort of external scrutiny, at least of the cases that have come to light that appear to have been given HIFU as a primary treatment for prostate cancer. I continue to be very concerned by what I see as the possible lack of duty of care for patients recommended to have HIFU – and as it has recently emerged that some patients appear to be suffering as a result, clearly this has to be taken extremely seriously. More cases of unconventional treatment are now coming to light and I believe we should be going back to look at the management of prostate cancer cases over the last four years or so.'

Happy with my statement, I duly signed it off.

I had chosen my words carefully and, fully aware that I was essentially alleging medical negligence, was sure that my statement would get a reaction. Sadly, following my interview with Dr Lamb, nothing really happened. Weeks went by, and then months, with the only thing becoming clear being that the transcripts of everyone interviewed had been shared with Mr Miller. This was carried out without our knowledge or consent and the result of this was that our fears of working in the department becoming more difficult were realised.

Perhaps as a consequence of working in such a pressured environment, elements of Mr Miller's practice became more irrational and our concerns became broader. Added at short notice to my operating list one day was a patient whose cystoscopy Mr Miller had carried out a week before when he had reported seeing only inflammation. This was peculiar because the patient had been admitted to intensive care two weeks previously with acute kidney failure, and a CT scan had shown a large bladder mass obstructing both kidneys. The kidney failure had been so bad that he had been dialysed and tubes called nephrostomies had been inserted directly into both kidneys. In this context, the thought that "cystitis" could be the underlying cause of all of this seemed extraordinary. The urology nurses picked up that this did not make sense and arranged for a repeat cystoscopy. When I looked in the bladder, I found the patient to have a large, solid tumour, a biopsy of which confirmed a high-grade muscle invasive bladder cancer. A bone scan showed spread to the bones and the patient sadly died three months later.

It was clear that the hospital's inability to deal with what seemed an obvious set of problems was having very real and harmful effects on patient care. The nurses and I were getting increasingly dismayed by our lack of progress in convincing the hospital management of our concerns. This was not least because many of the patients seen by Mr Miller were still on the wrong treatment path and at risk of suffering harm with every week that passed, and we wondered what else we could do.

The nurses came up with the idea of carrying out a formal review of a selection of Mr Miller's patients to provide hard data on what had happened to them. It was envisaged that this would lead to a written report that might help garner the hospital's attention. To help ensure impartiality and management buy-in, they approached Philip Kemp, one of their nursing colleagues who was also the Governance Manager for surgery. He immediately saw the value of doing a review and, on 15 July 2010, met with the Chief Nurse for surgery to discuss our concerns and the methodology of a review.

It was decided that Philip Kemp would carry out a look-back exercise on ten of Mr Miller's patients, looking specifically at their diagnosis, MDT outcome and treatment given. Following the meeting, the nurses forwarded to him the names of ten patients about whose management we had concerns.

While waiting for the completion of Philip Kemp's report, further concerns explicitly about the CNSs being deliberately excluded from consultations were raised at the routine cancer management meeting at which the Cancer Lead, the Cancer Lead Nurse and the CNSs were present. This practice, achieved either by patients being seen in peripheral clinics or by the CNSs being asked to leave the clinic room, had serious implications for patients because they would not have the benefit of CNS input with regard to receiving impartial advice on their treatment options either in person or in writing.

The nurses checked the letters from those clinics and confirmed that the same unorthodox practice continued; some of which broke the conditions that had been placed on Mr Miller by the Medical Director in April. An added new concern was that the term "HIFU" had been replaced in correspondence with words such as "new minimally invasive technique". We feared this would make it more difficult to track the patients' journeys and a future keyword search of the database would be less likely to identify the patients if we were ever to do a review of the sort we envisaged as necessary. In May, this specific concern – that the term "HIFU" in letters was being avoided – was raised.

Unfortunately, the Medical Director had no apparent mechanism to check that Mr Miller's practice was compliant with the various restrictions that had been placed on his practice, and as Clinical Lead I felt duty bound to raise a concern. I therefore went to see the Chief of Surgery and presented evidence that Mr Miller was not complying. The letter that followed, dated 16 July 2010, marked one of the low points of the hospital's handling of the affair up to this point. As Clinical Lead, I was copied into it, and I was incredulous as I read it.

"Dear Paul," it began, "…please can you kindly adhere to the points made in the letter of… thanks very much. Regards". Its friendly, matey and informal tone was entirely inappropriate and I found the lack of concern it displayed to be deeply troubling as I headed off for two weeks' annual leave.

Intrusive thoughts about the whole affair travelled with me on holiday and I had a difficult time sleeping and relaxing, let alone enjoying myself. On my return, in early August 2010, I went to see the Chief of Surgery and this time was unable to conceal my anger. I simply could not believe that, despite the mountain of evidence before them, they were still allowing the ongoing mistreatment of patients. My contemporaneous notes from that meeting are revealing.

'Would you be happy to see Mr Miller as a patient?', I asked.

After a pause he replied, 'No.'

'Then, how on earth', I continued, 'can you think it is appropriate for patients to see him?'

My notes describe how at that point the Chief merely laughed, I supposed nervously, but did not reply. I pointed out – again – that HIFU continued to be advocated contrary to guidelines and that several of the conditions for his continued practice that the Trust itself had stipulated, were being broken.

I left the room shaking, concerned that I had come over as being confrontational and that my actions might be counterproductive. But I need not have worried because a week later, on 17 August, at 10 a.m., I received a call from the Chief of Surgery stating that an external review had been arranged. He said it would be by Professor David Dearnaley, an oncologist at the Royal Marsden Hospital, and he mentioned two possible dates.

On 23 August 2010, at 6 p.m. I knocked on the Medical Director's door. I wanted to confirm the date of the review because I would need to make time for it and prepare. I went into her office and was immediately struck by the number of documents on her desk and the air of disorder in the room. I asked her about the external review, mentioned the possible dates given to me by the Chief and asked what was going to happen. She apologised, became tearful and, worryingly, called me 'Paul'. She was clearly not coping. No external review had been arranged and I couldn't see any prospect of one being arranged any time soon. I left the room and went home feeling gloomy.

Concerns were reported not just from within the hospital but from other routes. At that time, each urology department periodically had to undergo a review of its practice by a group of clinicians outside the Trust; the so-called external peer review. This process happened every few years, and their remit, broadly, was to ensure that the provision of cancer services was at least adequate, to reassure Commissioners that minimum standards were being met and to point out where improvements could perhaps be made. They needed assurance that there was compliance with, for example, the nationally set minimum number of pelvic cancer operations per surgeon. On 6 September 2010, the department underwent routine external peer review of our cancer services. Their assessments carried weight and so it was significant that they reported concerns that the Cancer Lead for urology, Mr Miller, had not made himself available for the meeting and went on to question his commitment to the role. No action was taken by the Trust.

Despite the fact that the rest of us had been interviewed by Dr Lamb months beforehand, it was not until September 2010 that Mr

Miller was interviewed by her. Records show that, on 22 September 2010, the Lamb internal report was produced, but frustratingly this was not known to anyone in the department and the contents were not disclosed to or discussed with the contributors.

There was by now a new Chief of Surgery in post, an anaesthetist, who I went to see for information on the report. Unfortunately, none was forthcoming. In fact, I was never told of the outcome of the report, nor its conclusions – and was rather embarrassed some years later to be quizzed on it while in the witness stand in Coroner's court, when I had to say to the astonished QC who was asking me about its details that I had never even seen it, nor been told anything about its contents or conclusions despite being Head of Department at the time.

I repeatedly went to see the new Chief of Surgery in her office by the Intensive Care Unit. Dismayed that she didn't seem to know much about the clinical concerns we had and the difficulties we were facing, I ran through them, emphasising the seriousness of the situation and urging her to go and speak to my medical and nursing colleagues to get their view. She seemed unsure what to do and, with no change in the situation, I came to the realisation that I would have to go back to speak to her line manager, the Medical Director. The Medical Director I had seen a few weeks before had resigned soon after I had seen her and there was now a new (interim) in post, so I went to see him.

Unfortunately, he knew nothing whatsoever of the situation and seemed unreceptive. I was left in the invidious position of having difficulty persuading the two key people in the chain of command, both of whom were new in post, of taking me seriously when I described what seemed so clear to many of us – the significant ongoing issue of patient safety in the urology department.

I learned some years later the important point that Dr Lamb's report had in fact concluded that there was indeed evidence that Mr Miller did not appropriately discuss HIFU therapy or alternative treatment options with patients. Dr Lamb made several recommendations, including that the number of patients referred for HIFU should be determined together with the appropriateness of each decision and outcome for each patient. The report went on to suggest that further investigation was required, including expert opinion.

Ironically, external expert review was what I had sought and been promised by the previous Medical Director at the beginning of the year. Although we were completely in the dark about Dr Lamb's report, to the extent that we did not know when it had been completed let alone its contents and conclusions, the nurses had stayed in close touch with Philip Kemp and so we knew that he would soon complete his report.

Indeed, on 11 October 2010, Philip Kemp completed his report following his look-back exercise into Mr Miller's practice, and showed it to the CNSs and me. He submitted it to the interim Medical Director, the Chief of Surgery, the Chief Nurse and the Trust Head of Patient Safety. There was a new Chief Executive in post. He requested the report and was also given it. The report described how ten patients had been studied and, for each, the history was summarised together with the diagnosis and MDT decision. In the final column the actual treatment given was listed.

He found that Mr Miller had not followed MDT advice in eight out of ten cases. In the other two, there was insufficient documentation to come to a firm conclusion. The patients were on unconventional treatment pathways; many of them having been put on hormones waiting for a business case to be approved for HIFU and had not received any definitive treatment at all. Furthermore, he concluded that six patients were likely to have suffered harm as a result of their management, a further three may have suffered harm and in the last it was not possible to determine.

It was clear that patient A, who had tragically developed metastatic prostate cancer while waiting for treatment and whose complaint had been raised as an SUI was far from isolated because there was a pattern of precisely the same mismanagement in numerous other patients. The report also described the highly unorthodox practice of patients being approached by Mr Miller prior to the MDT and clinic appointment, some of whom were given literature on HIFU. The report recommended that Mr Miller be suspended immediately from all NHS work and referred to the

General Medical Council (GMC) for investigation. Phillip Kemp also recommended that there be a formal review of all patients treated by Mr Miller for prostate cancer.

I read the report open-mouthed, as its findings and conclusions were exactly in line with the feelings of the department. At last, we thought, now that there was unequivocal evidence that multiple patients had been harmed, the senior managers would have to act.

Unfortunately, the Trust took a different view and, unbelievably to my mind, no action was taken.

It is difficult to overestimate the negative effect that raising concerns has when those concerns are not adequately listened to or acted upon. Not just on me but on the wider team. Many of us were struggling to keep things together and we could not know that things were going to get a whole lot worse, not least due to a further deterioration in behaviour and practice.

I started noticing that cancer patients in greater numbers were being transferred from Mr Miller's care to either mine or Mr Rane's. I asked Cathy, the Lead Nurse in urology, who looked a bit sheepish. 'To be honest,' she said, 'I transfer them over to you or Abhay when I think it's not really safe for them to stay where they are.'

I persisted with the new Chief of Surgery by going to see her many times in her office with specific examples of patient misman-agement. Cathy told her about transferring patients on to my and Abhay's operating lists. I asked her what the Trust was doing about the Kemp report, but she seemed unsure. In some of the meetings she was sympathetic and I came away from them with the impression that the Trust might act, but, as the weeks went by, nothing happened and it was all very similar to my experience with her predecessor.

With a distinct sense of déjà vu, I decided to bypass the Chief of Surgery and went a number of times to see the new (interim) Medical Director. We discussed the fact that the Kemp report had demonstrated actual patient harm and I gave him further examples of specific patient mismanagement – one of which would be raised as another SUI. He was only filling in temporarily until a new permanent replacement could be found and seemed reluctant to act.

After several conversations with him, he eventually, grudgingly, agreed to arrange an external review.

Four weeks went by, during which I had heard nothing, and, passing him in the main hospital corridor one morning in December 2010, I asked him what was happening about the review. He said he hadn't found anyone and furthermore that he was unable to find someone to do it.

'You have to wonder why that is,' he added, quizzically. He seemed to be implying either that there was not much substance to what we were saying or perhaps that it was "political" or nuanced in some way.

I found this profoundly troubling: he had been a recipient of the Kemp report, which was entirely clear that the hospital had a major issue of patient safety. He had told me a few weeks before that he would arrange for an external review, and now, having failed to do this, it seemed he might not now be arranging one after all. I persisted and asked for a formal meeting with him, which was arranged for two weeks later.

On this occasion, I made sure that I was accompanied by Abhay and Kate to make him understand that the concerns were widespread. We went through all the issues one by one and, after some time, he agreed (again) to arrange an external review. We left the meeting relieved and, over a coffee later that morning, discussed what we thought would happen next. The glaring unknown was whether he would actually follow through this time and do what he said he would.

CHAPTER 3

2011- 2013

THE NEW YEAR STARTED AND, unsure if and when the external review might take place, we decided that we must continue to pass on our concerns to the management. The CNSs, Kate and Catherine, met with the Chief of Surgery in early 2011 to describe their anxieties that not only were many patients now receiving the wrong treatment, some were being referred out of network to a variety of hospitals, counter to agreed, commissioned pathways. They emphasised the inconvenience and delay this practice was creating for patients, together with the added problem that patients could not easily be tracked through their treatment journey. They were told to make a formal complaint in writing, the Chief of Surgery seemingly continuing to be unaware of the fact that raising concerns about patient care was not something that needed be put in writing. Perhaps intimidated by possible repercussions, they decided not to.

Meanwhile, the original SUI of patient A still rumbled on. At the end of the previous year, in November 2010, there had been an exchange of emails between the Head of Patient Safety and various hospital managers highlighting that it had now been a full nine months since the complaint had been raised by the patient. That same day, the interim Medical Director decided on a plan to present the case to the management board meeting early the following year. Unfortunately, no discernible action was taken by the Trust, other than a "being open" meeting would be held with the patient and his wife.

A new Medical Director was appointed in early 2011 and met with Phillip Kemp to discuss his report.

'You have to be careful. You are dealing with a Consultant's career and reputation,' the Medical Director allegedly told Philip Kemp, who soon after left the Trust very suddenly for alternative employment elsewhere.

The Medical Director was later to state in his written evidence for the Coroner's court: "When investigating concerns regarding clinical staff my priority is to ensure patient safety. However, I also have to balance this with (the fact that) unfounded allegations against a clinician can cause lasting damage to that person's reputation and career". Sadly, he seemed to be entirely missing the point: there were no *unfounded* allegations at all, but rather a series of numerous specific examples of actual patient harm.

In early March 2011, the external opinion into the appropriateness of HIFU for patient A was received. It stated that HIFU would not have been an appropriate treatment for the patient and went on to say that not offering radiotherapy was "unusual". The Medical Director asked Dr Lamb to "pull together" this opinion from the external consultant, together with her report. She did this and concluded, unsurprisingly, that the patient should have been offered radiotherapy.

On 16 March 2011, the "being open" meeting was held between the Medical Director, patient A and his wife. I bumped into the Medical Director shortly afterwards and enquired how it had gone. He responded that it had gone well and then added that he thought that it had all been a misunderstanding because Mr Miller claimed that, when he had said "zapping" the prostate to the patient, he was referring to radiotherapy. In the context of the external Consultant saying that it was unusual for the patient *not* to have been offered radiotherapy and Dr Lamb's concluding that the patient *should have been* offered radiotherapy this seemed a surprising conclusion to come to. I was about to point this out when I remembered patient A's statement.

'So why did Mr Miller tell the patient he was on a waiting list for the machine to be rented in?' I asked, adding, 'There is no waiting list for radiotherapy and you certainly don't have to rent in a radiotherapy machine.'

'Well, I admit that is odd, as the patient's wife is clear that they were told he was on a waiting list and would be done when the hospital could rent in the machine,' he replied.

'Well, there you have it,' I said. 'You don't rent in radiotherapy machines,' I repeated. 'He was clearly talking about HIFU.'

He didn't respond to that and I walked away from our interaction with an immense sense of frustration, or perhaps anger, utterly incredulous that the Medical Director seemed to have been so easily misled.

I took solace in the good news filtering through at this time that there would indeed be an external review. Early in 2011, the interim Medical Director had met with the Chief Nurse and the Chief of Surgery to work on terms of reference for the external review of Mr Miller's practice. An external reviewer was finally found, terms were agreed in February 2011 and a date was set for the visit – 24 March 2011.

As the date drew closer, we became anxious that we had heard practically nothing from the Trust about it. We did not know what background information the reviewer had been given, nor what his precise remit was. We assumed that he would have been given a copy of the Kemp and Lamb reports but wondered also whether he had been given specific examples of patients about whom we had raised concerns beyond those featuring in the two reports.

Due to the lack of information surrounding his visit, and realising its importance, the CNSs Kate and Catherine assembled key clinical letters from some of the patients we were concerned about. In all there were twenty-six. They bought a red ring binder and carefully hole punched and clipped all the letters into it and made arrangements for the external reviewer to be given it. We just hoped that he would have had time to read it prior to the interviews.

On 24 March 2011, Professor Neal, a Consultant Urologist working in Cambridge, duly arrived to carry out his review. He was to interview all key members of the department at half hour intervals, and it was made clear at the start of my interview early in the morning that I only had thirty minutes. He started by asking me about my job plan, then went on to the structure of my clinics, something about the on-call rota, and so on.

After a while, I sneaked a look at the clock and felt uneasy that more than half my time had gone. I interrupted his flow of questions to say that I thought the reason he had been asked to come was to look at the concerns many of us had about safety in the department, including the management of patients. He was visibly irritated and, pushing across the desk a copy of the terms of reference for his visit for me to read, said that he hadn't been brought in to do that at all. The terms of reference asked him to look at a number of generic issues to do with the department, clinics, on calls, and so on, a bit about pathways but not much else. My fears that this might all prove to be a waste of time were compounded when it became clear he had not even heard of the Kemp and Lamb reports and therefore knew nothing about them. The onus, it seemed, would be on us to get our points across despite the fact that the external reviewer wanted – understandably, given his remit – to focus on other, rather mundane issues.

I could see the red folder in front of him on the desk and gestured towards it.

'What about that, though?' I enquired.

'This? Well, they have all been mismanaged.'

He opened the folder and flicked through it, and I could see where he had written his thoughts on the letters. We discussed one or two of them and he clearly shared our concerns. By late afternoon, all key members of the department had been interviewed, except one, as Mr Miller had declared himself unable to attend.

It had been a stressful and difficult day, not least because the review had been shoehorned into a normal busy day with no reduction of clinical activity. Frustratingly, the Trust had no intention of giving any feedback until some of us insisted and, at about 6 p.m. the Chief of Surgery was dispatched down to the Urology office to speak to us. She stated that the verbal feedback from Professor Neal was, 'You've got a real problem here.'

In the following days, I spoke to the Medical Director, who echoed those words and, on two separate occasions over the following weeks, the new CEO used exactly those words when recounting to me what Professor Neal had said to them both on the day of the interviews. I was relieved we must have managed to get our points across and was optimistic that the Trust would get on and do something without further delay.

A few weeks later, Professor Neal's draft report arrived and the Chief of Surgery invited me to look at it. First, I read his summary of my interview. It stated that "Mr Swinn reported concerns from within the department regarding the use of HIFU with regard to his belief that patients were not being counselled in a neutral way regarding standard management options".

This was accurate and consistent with what had been concluded by the Lamb report. It described my concerns regarding the ownership of the HIFU machine and of patients being transferred to the private sector for treatment. It also stated that I and other clinicians he interviewed throughout the day shared a concern that patients had been started on Bicalutamide hormone treatment while a business case was being developed for HIFU. It was a good summary of my position and I was pleased that I had got my points across.

Next, I looked at the conclusions. It stated that the department's concerns should be investigated by means of a further external review of Mr Miller's practice by a panel comprising suitably qualified experts and a lay person. Such a panel, it stated, "is to be found through the Royal College of Surgeons' 'Independent Review Mechanism (IRM)'". I was mightily relieved as I read this, which, together with the verbal feedback he had given to the Chief Executive and Medical Director on the day, surely meant that the Trust would now act.

I spoke to both the Chief Executive and the Medical Director. An IRM was the logical next step and would allow us to draw a line under this whole episode and get the patients back on the right track. Surely they would now be arranging an IRM? Sadly not, as the Chief Executive wanted to wait for the final report. While I could see his logic, and no doubt he wanted to protect himself and his organisation legally, I felt strongly that he was being unreasonably cautious, especially in the context of time being so critical for patients. Professor Neal could not complete his report until he had interviewed Mr Miller, which I envisaged might be difficult to arrange. Surely they had enough evidence to proceed with an IRM, given what was at stake?

In the event, it took more than three months for Professor Neal to meet up with Mr Miller (informally at a Urology conference in Liverpool in the last week of June 2011). His final report was issued a couple of weeks later, stating that he had adjusted it to fit in more with his brief. It was a watered-down version, more cautious in tone and less unambiguous than the draft. It did indeed reflect more accurately his terms of reference but the section about the need to investigate Mr Miller further was still there, albeit preceded by the word "if": "*If* the Trust is to investigate Mr Miller further..." and then followed the same description of the IRM of the RCS.

There was still enough in the report and verbal feedback to bring about resolution of the matter either by the Trust initiating an IRM or by investigating further some of the other issues brought up in the report to do with behaviour and relationships. Notably, Professor Neal's covering email to the Chief Executive, Medical Director and Chief of Surgery stated: "He (*Mr Miller*) remains concerned that allegations of promoting people into HIFU .... have been raised again although previous investigations (he tells me) did not support these allegations".

Anyone with knowledge of this affair reading this would have spotted the obvious inconsistency since previous investigations: both Philip Kemp's look-back exercise of ten patients and the Lamb report *had* in fact demonstrated inappropriate bias towards HIFU, with the look-back exercise citing at least six people having been harmed as a direct result.

Time went by without feedback from the managers and it gradually became clear that they were not doing anything. The problem of mismanagement of patients continued and, worryingly, Mr Miller seemed to have a new found confidence. It would not be until 2019 that I would learn that, following Professor Neal's visit and report, the Medical Director met with the Cancer Lead and agreed that they "should clarify Mr Miller's responsibilities and give him the chance to prove himself as Cancer Lead for Urology".

Furthermore, the Medical Director wrote to Mr Miller actually *apologising* to him for the length of time the SUI investigation had taken and exonerating him on everything except the external consultant's critical opinion of him in not offering the patient radiotherapy. Regarding that last issue, he went on to say that he would ask the reviewer to discuss it with Mr Miller.

It is difficult to view this action by the still new Medical Director as anything other than a massive error of judgement and, had I been aware of it at the time, I would have resigned my post and I suspect other members of staff would have done the same. When the Medical Director eventually told me that the Trust would not be doing anything following the external review, I felt desperately sad and frustrated but, most important of all, anxious that this problem might never get resolved. Dealing with this issue was taking its toll on me and my family life and, as much as I tried to put it out of my mind to some extent, recurring thoughts and themes would just not go away. I tried meditation and exercise but, however hard I tried, I often found myself wide awake by 2 a.m. with little prospect of any further sleep.

Patient A sadly died of prostate cancer in 2012 and to my mind there was overwhelming evidence that he had died due to medical mismanagement. This was of course profoundly disturbing and I just could not fathom the Trust's inaction. I thought of the external opinion for the SUI stating HIFU would have been inappropriate and how the "being open" meeting had brought with it attempts to make out that the patient was mistaken about the treatment he had been offered. I thought about how Phillip Kemp's look-back exercise confirming MDT decisions had been ignored, and concluded that at least six patients had been harmed as a result. I thought of Professor Neal's verbal feedback to the Medical Director and the Chief Executive, his recommendation to investigate this issue further and his statement to me on the twenty-six patients in the red folder that they had "all been mismanaged".

My concern was that, if the Trust was not going to act now, it might never – and inevitably more patients would suffer and more would inevitably die. As Clinical Lead, I felt a great responsibility to continue my efforts and went to see the Medical Director repeatedly, often accompanied by Abhay. We continued to implore him to do something, and his responses varied. On some occasions, he would say, or at least imply, that he would look at it, but on other occasions he seemed distracted or perhaps fed up to be talking about the same issues time and again.

We told him about new patients being mismanaged, and this included a man, patient B, whose death seemed particularly worrying. The nurses came to me one afternoon saying that while looking for a set of patient notes they had come across another set of notes tucked away under a desk, apparently deliberately hidden. They read the notes and it seemed to them that the patient had been mismanaged and perhaps had died as a result. On reading the notes, I came to the same conclusion and so went to see the Medical Director to tell him of our concerns.

He looked worried. 'Can you get me the notes please?' he asked.

I paused and pointed out where they were.

'To be clear,' I said, 'are you instructing me to go into a Consultant colleague's office and remove something without his knowledge?'

'Yes.'

So I went down immediately, retrieved the notes and within minutes was back in the Medical Director's office where I handed them to him, convinced that this would spur them into action.

Unfortunately, nothing happened. I allowed six weeks to go by before going back again to see the Medical Director. I asked him what he had done about the set of notes I had given him. 'What set of notes?' he asked.

'You know. The patient who died,' I said, and, trying my best to stay calm, described the incident of me telling him about the patient and his instruction to me to go and retrieve the notes for him to see.

He looked puzzled. 'I don't have any recollection of that.'

Feeling numb and angry, I left his office and went back to theatre to do my operating list, although finding it difficult to concentrate. What else could I do? I wondered, and decided that I must see the Chief Executive to tell him of my concerns regarding his Medical Director's inaction.

A few days later, having established the Chief Executive's timetable for the day from his personal assistant, I hovered outside his office and managed to catch him between meetings. I told him that I was very worried about the ongoing safety problems in Urology and was very concerned that the Medical Director didn't seem to be taking the issues seriously. He waited until I had finished and reassured me that he was 'a very good Medical Director – he will do the right thing.'

I replied by saying that he didn't actually seem to be doing anything about it at all.

'Don't worry. He will do the right thing,' he repeated, fixing me with a stare.

I have kicked myself repeatedly since for accepting his words so readily, because the situation not only continued but deteriorated. In August 2011, the nurses raised concerns regarding Mr Miller's cystoscopy practice with the Chief Nurse, who passed them on to the Medical Director. On 4 August 2011, a report of a missed bladder cancer was made to the Medical Director and was soon raised as another SUI. The following month, September 2011, an internal validation report was submitted to the Urology MDT criticising Mr Miller's leadership and his poor attendance at it, and the Cancer Lead wrote to Mr Miller on 5 December reminding him of his responsibilities as MDT Lead.

Some of that was unknown to me at that time, but what was clear was that unacceptably low standards of practice, some of it difficult to explain, continued. On 24 November 2011, a very fit man in his early fifties, patient C, was discussed at the Urology MDT. He had previously been treated for high-grade bladder cancer by Mr Miller in the private sector and the same cancer had now returned. This was now in a very serious situation and the conventional treatment was clear – he should be offered a cystectomy, i.e. total bladder removal, aimed at curing him. Indeed, that was the decision of the MDT and, when the case was discussed more widely at the sMDT a few days later, the decision was ratified with the exact words of the region's bladder cancer specialists written down verbatim in the patient's notes: "strongly advise to go straight to cystectomy".

Worryingly, that advice was not followed and, when the patient was seen in clinic, he was referred to a hospital in Watford for photodynamic therapy (PDT). This was not then – and is not now – a treatment for bladder cancer, Watford was not a standard hospital for us to refer to and PDT was not even something they offered. Realising that the patient was at risk of progression of disease, the nurses insisted on meeting the Cancer Lead to discuss this case and the context of their ongoing concerns. They met him on 12 December 2011 and, on 14 December 2011, he emailed the Medical Director and Chief Nurse about the concerns.

Much was going on but there seemed to be nobody in overall charge of the various issues. Nobody except the Urology team had oversight and knowledge of what was happening, including the increasingly irrational management decisions. We were doing our bit by raising concerns time and again through the right channels, at some significant detriment to our working environment, our general sense of well-being and even health, but nobody higher up the chain seemed to be listening or acting. Our concerns regarding the lack of leadership on this issue were echoed elsewhere and, in December 2011, the Cancer Lead Nurse reported to the Chief of Surgery the concerns that "no one was coordinating the different SUIs, complaints and investigations".

The Cancer Lead set up a telephone meeting with Mr Miller to discuss the various ongoing concerns. This happened at 2.30 p.m. on 16 December and proved to be an acrimonious discussion. The Cancer Lead's contemporaneous notes of the conversation describe Mr Miller as being "very put out" that his authority was being questioned, that he claimed to be "the only person in the MDT to know the right treatment for patients" and that he could offer "any treatment he wanted to, even without MDT approval".

All of this would have rung very loud alarm bells with the Cancer Lead, who was well aware that MDTs had been set up, at least in part, to eliminate maverick practice through achieving a consensus way forward for the management of cancer patients; the collective view being paramount. The Cancer Lead passed the information on to the Medical Director, who replied on 28 December that he would set up a meeting in January 2012 regarding concerns about Mr Miller.

On 5 January 2012, the Medical Director, Chief Nurse, Cancer Lead, Chief of Surgery and Cancer Lead Nurse met to discuss concerns regarding Mr Miller, and concluded, extraordinarily some might think, that there were no new concerns. I received an email from the Medical Director on 13 January, copied to the Chief of Surgery, the Cancer Lead and the Chief Executive, which read: "Whilst I completely recognize that feelings around Paul (Miller) run high, we have closed the SUI in relation to (patient A) and I have met with (patient A)'s son in order to do this. There is a case of the man who the MDT decided should have a cystectomy (I have been told) but was offered a very different treatment. This case is being looked at separately. It is not acceptable in terms of HR practice to have yet another meeting about Paul with Paul not there". The email went on to say, "It is my very firmly held belief that we now need a meeting with all the key stakeholders .... to set expectations going forward for how all members of the department will behave".

This email from the Medical Director seemed to me an attempt to draw a line under everything, to discourage me from meeting with him further (at least without Mr Miller being present) and seemed to hint at my emotional state ("feelings running high"). Needless to say, I did not appreciate it, nor his insistence on how "all" members of the department should behave. However, I drew reassurance by his statement that patient C would be looked into.

For weeks, nothing discernible happened regarding patient C. Knowing him to be at significant risk, the nurses again approached the Cancer Lead in early 2012 to reiterate their concerns. Despite his email to me at the start of the year, I went back to see the Medical Director a number of times, often accompanied by Mr Rane. Surely there was a clear patient safety issue, we said, and added that we failed to understand why he was not acting. On one such visit, getting on for a year since Professor Neal's visit, he muttered about lack of evidence and lack of specific examples.

With that I became agitated. 'What do you mean lack of examples?' I snapped, exasperatedly. 'You have dozens now – what about the twenty-six patients in the red folder for a start?'

He stopped and looked around him and then reached up to the top of his filing cabinet and pulled down the red folder. It was filthy, and he blew hard on it and the resultant cloud of thick dust engulfed the three of us.

'This folder?', he asked.

'Yes, that folder.'

The Medical Director was aware of the Kemp report, the Lamb report, the patients with missed bladder tumours, the reports of poor behaviour, including some of falsifying the patient record, the SUIs, the twenty-six patients in the red folder, the verbal feedback from Professor Neal and his (thirty-nine as it turned out) written critical comments on many of the twenty-six patients, and of other patients that Abhay and I had brought before him, including patient B, whose death seemed suspicious and whose notes I had handed him personally.

But still nothing happened.

Unsurprisingly, I and my colleagues became increasingly despondent and it was proving, for me at least, difficult to concentrate at work. Even when at home I found it difficult to think about anything else. My difficulty sleeping was worsening and I had resorted to alcohol to help distract me and get off to sleep. I still continued to wake at about 2 a.m., though, and had taken to wandering around the house in the small hours so that my restlessness would not disturb Lesley. Time off was dominated by thoughts of what was going on at work, and holidays were clouded by the issue. I just couldn't see why they couldn't see what we could. The impact it was having on me and my loved ones was brought home to me one day by my mother, who took me to one side during a visit imploring me to sort out whatever problem I had at work 'as whatever it is is effecting your relationship with your family.'

I had frequent discussions with the CNSs, Lead Nurse, Abhay and other medical colleagues. Why was the hospital not acting? Had we missed something? Was there some weird dynamic somehow making us egg each other on? Was this a personal issue, a power struggle? Could Mr Miller be ill? We went through each of these hypotheses time and again, looking at the evidence afresh. And each time we came up with the same conclusion – we were right and the hospital had just got it very wrong, and tragically so.

I had gone all the way up through the medical management hierarchy to CEO level and the nurses had been through the nursing hierarchy and still they wouldn't listen. The nurses thought that they should go all the way to the top and arranged to meet the CEO too. They duly told him of their concerns but came away despondent because he told them more evidence was needed. Good grief, we thought, how much do they need?!

Well, we decided, if they want more evidence, let's give it to them if that's what it takes. The nurses obtained the hospital notes of eight further patients whom we believed to have been mismanaged. For each, the nurses typed out a summary of the care given followed by a bullet point list of the concerns we had regarding management. This was completed for each of the eight and the summary was then stapled to the front of each set of notes. They discussed the key issues with the Lead Nurse when they handed the notes to her. She said that she would take the sets of notes to the Medical Director and make sure that action was taken. I was relieved to hear this and even more so when we spotted the sets of notes in the Medical Director's office, on the floor next to his desk.

Weeks and then months went by with nothing discernible happening, and we were perplexed as to why this would be. After all, they had requested more evidence and had been provided it in an accessible form – to the extent that the Medical Director didn't even need to open the notes to look inside. Every now and then, one of this cohort of patients would have an outpatient appointment and the notes would have to be retrieved temporarily, often by the nurses, from the Medical Director's office, so we knew for sure they were still there and were generally optimistic that something now would happen.

I wrestled with whether I should keep going back to see the Medical Director – it was difficult to get the right balance between, on the one hand leaving him to get on with his job of looking at the evidence we had given him, and on the other hand going back to make it clear that this problem was not going to go away by itself. However, on one such visit to see him in 2012, the Medical Director told me that he had come round to accepting the need for a proper external review through an IRM, as suggested by Professor Neal. My relief lasted only seconds because he soon added that it wouldn't be happening because clinicians have to give their consent to such an investigation and Mr Miller had declined to do so.

'What we need', he added breezily, 'is more evidence!'

I was incredulous as I again ran through the wealth of evidence before them, including the twenty-six patients in the red folder. His response was that they had already been looked at and so they did not constitute new evidence. I told him clearly that they had not been looked at or sorted out and that undoubtedly some had been given the wrong treatment and could yet be put on to more orthodox, suitable treatment pathways.

I added to this by reminding him of the verbal feedback from Professor Neal on the day of his visit that the Trust had "a real problem here". I trotted out other examples of evidence they had been given. 'And now you're telling me he won't agree to a review of his practice?' I sought to control my voice, which I realised was raised. 'Surely, that's a red flag if ever there was one.' I thought that I had perhaps overstepped the mark by being so overtly critical of him and left his office before saying something I would regret.

More months went by without any discernible change and I became ever more disillusioned. The managers next made nonsensical changes to the structure of the department, which included scrapping the Urology Lead Nurse role. They did not listen to me regarding my opposition on that issue and certainly were clearly not listening to me about the main, basic problem of patient safety, and I therefore made the decision to resign my post as Head of Department. It had been a post I had held for almost six years and, although I had made some significant progress in some key areas, I was just not getting through to them on the important issues. I was also paying a high price for it personally and I surmised perhaps Abhay, the next Clinical Lead, would have more luck.

In truth, it was some years since I had derived any significant pleasure from my job in the broadest sense. Throughout my career, I had enjoyed the camaraderie and support that comes from working as part of a team but that had long since disappeared, replaced by an antagonistic, stressful and unhappy environment. A gloom had seeped in that was affecting all aspects of my life, and I realise, looking back on it, that at this time I had lost the essence of what it is to be a doctor.

I had always enjoyed speaking to people in clinic but now even the odd story from my soldier patients failed to lift my spirits much. Operating, from which I had derived great pleasure ever since being introduced to it in Jamaica, had become mundane and ceased to interest me. My mind frequently flicked back to the simpler, more honest approach to health care I had experienced there, where I first encountered life as a hospital surgeon. But, with the current working environment of mounting serious concerns continuing to be unchallenged by those in charge, I became ever more disillusioned.

My colleague Mr Rane followed me as Clinical Lead and continued to raise concerns about the ongoing problems on behalf of the department. Concerns were raised about other aspects of practice too – one about a training Registrar left to complete a difficult operation unsupervised; the patient suffered a complication and had to be transferred out to another hospital for specialist support. Another SUI, on a different matter, was raised in October 2012 and investigated in 2013. These issues attracted the attention of the Patient Safety Manager, who, in June 2013, subsequent records demonstrate, once again showed the Medical Director Philip Kemp's look-back exercise of the ten patients.

Although difficult to achieve, many of us knew the importance of maintaining cordial professional relationships at work and were able to maintain a semblance of professionalism on a day-to-day basis. Much of what was going on therefore rumbled away under the surface but occasionally matters would bubble up in unpleasant style.

In July 2013, a patient was discussed at the sMDT in Guildford, at which I was present. The case was a man with an uncommon tumour affecting part of the bladder, and the sMDT decided to offer him a clinic appointment to discuss the standard, conventional treatment for this condition: a partial cystectomy, i.e. removal of part of the bladder with the tumour in it. When I fed that information back to the local MDT later that day, Mr Miller became angry and refused to allow the patient to be seen at Guildford, saying he would arrange a PET scan (a scan similar to a CT) and see the patient himself.

This troubled the nurses, not least because they knew that Mr Miller was away the following day and for the two weeks after that, and so a delay would ensue. One of them phoned me in the afternoon to express her concerns and I telephoned the Medical Director for advice. He asked me why Mr Miller could not see the patient the following day. I replied that it was because he was going to watch cricket. Little did I know then that this honest reply to a simple question, innocently made, would later be distorted and used against me by the most senior of hospital managers.

The same month, July 2013, the MDT discussed a patient who had undergone HIFU and whose prostate-specific antigen (PSA) was rising. This meant that the patient had recurrent disease, and the MDT recommended an MRI scan. The Registrar saw the patient in clinic and arranged the scan but Mr Miller intervened by phoning the patient and switching the scan to the local private hospital. When the patient questioned this, saying he no longer had health insurance, he was reassured there would be no charge as he was a trial patient. 'I had no idea I was in a trial!', the patient later said.

This was very concerning on several levels, not least because it seemed as if the patient had been diverted away from the scrutiny of the MDT. The Trust's Surgery Governance and Risk Manager was asked to investigate and reported her concerns to the Medical Director and the Chief Executive.

On 19 September 2013, following two (non-clinical) incidents, the hospital management suspended Mr Miller. What worried me was that the period of suspension of only two weeks would scarcely be enough time for the hospital to get to grips with what was going on and it seemed more like a punishment or gesture rather than something meaningful. It was soon extended somewhat and I was sure that a manager would be contacting some of us for statements about our concerns and with a plan to review the patients who were still on the wrong treatment pathways. But, in the event, nothing discernible happened during that time and a date was set for Mr Miller to return at the end of November.

* * *

In April 2013, I had started working part time at the Royal Surrey County Hospital, Guildford. The wrangling about cancer centres had finally come to an end with the decision that Guildford would be the designated site within our network of cancer hospitals for cystectomies. I was asked to split my time between the two Trusts and was very happy to be a part of developing a new enterprise. The plan was to do cystectomies with minimally invasive techniques using a robot. This was new to me and meant that I required further training. I was very grateful to the Urological Foundation for offering a scholarship to enable me to visit the world-renowned Keck Hospital of the University of Southern California in November 2013 to observe Dr Inderbir Gill and his colleagues, who ran the robotic programme there.

My routine in Los Angeles was to get up very early, have breakfast and be at the hospital shortly after 7 a.m. I was by myself, the change of scene was welcome, and I decided to use the time to come to a decision about what to do about the situation at home. Einstein's definition of insanity – doing the same thing over and over again and expecting a different result – kept nagging away at me. Mr Miller had been suspended but the truth was that he would be back soon, and I had no confidence that anything much would change.

Given the early starts there, I gave myself the odd afternoon off and, about halfway through my time in LA, sat by the swimming pool to think about all the evidence we had put before the most senior hospital managers. I tried to quantify what we had achieved, and the answer was, well, not very much. Arguably, there was a safer environment for patients in some respects, with fewer patients being channelled down the wrong route, but unacceptable practices continued, as exemplified by the recent apparent diverting of a patient with a poor outcome away from the MDT.

I thought of the personal cost in terms of how it had affected me and my family and also stunted my career. I thought of how tired I was of it all, mentally and physically, and shuddered at the thought of going home to more sleepless nights. After no more than an hour or so I came to a conclusion: I would drop the subject. The literally dozens of conversations I had had with the most senior managers in the hospital had led to a couple of investigations to which I had contributed, but nothing had persuaded the hospital to act. I concluded that I had done far more than most would have done in this situation and that the failure to gain traction with the management was due to a variety of factors outside my control. In this context, continuing seemed painful as well as futile.

I enjoyed the rest of my time in LA and felt a sense of freedom I had not experienced for some years. Oddly, I felt physically lighter and, during my last week there, seemed more or less to skip around. The news programme in the plane on the way home covered the fiftieth anniversary of the assassination of JFK and, despite being shrouded in darkness and fog on arrival back in the UK, I felt more positive than I had for some considerable time.

Then, at my first MDT after returning, a familiar patient was presented – patient C, the man with recurrent bladder cancer whom we felt had been mismanaged. The nurses had flagged him up to the Cancer Lead, who had escalated it to the Medical Director within days. Needless to say, no action had been taken. Now, very sadly, in Mr Miller's absence, a locum had looked into patient C's bladder and found high-grade, high-stage bladder cancer. Furthermore, the imaging which we were now looking at in the MDT showed that the disease had spread outside the bladder, and the man, aged only in his mid-fifties, would die from it.

Not for the first time, the mood of the MDT was sombre, but this time the anger among many was palpable. I felt the eyes of various of my colleagues on me, and I realised that I simply could not ignore it. I left the MDT and went straight upstairs to the Medical Director's office. His door was ajar and with a quick tap I walked in. I summarised the case, making it clear where the patient had been mismanaged; not least by ignoring the outcome of both the local and sMDTs. I pointed out that the patient was otherwise fit and well and that it was likely that he would die, and probably very soon, and that all of this could have been prevented. 'Another man is going to die who shouldn't,' were my exact words.

The Medical Director stopped and listened and then said, 'Sounds like you better fill in a Datix form.'

A form? Fill out a form? To be put with all the other thousands of forms that the Trust gets every year and either does or does not act on? Shocked into silence, at that moment all of the frustration and anger and resentment that I had endured now for many years surfaced. I could have shouted or screamed or hit him or smashed my fist on his crappy little desk, but I didn't. I didn't do any of these things. What I did do was to start crying. I tried stifling my emotions, but it was no good, and I left his room and trotted down the stairs, desperately trying to calm down and make myself look presentable before re-entering the MDT meeting.

Another more or less entirely sleepless night followed; never great on a Thursday with an overbooked all-day operating list in prospect the following day. I somehow got through the list; my mind mostly elsewhere. When leaving just before 7 p.m., I could see the light still on in the Chief Executive's office and I decided to go and see him.

His door was open.

'Ah, come in Mr Swinn,' he said, welcoming me in as he swung his chair round, inviting me to take a seat with an expansive hand gesture. 'How can I help?'

I told him how another man was going to die despite it being entirely preventable had orthodox treatment pathways been followed. 'Furthermore,' I said, 'It's the CQC visit next week and I am going to meet them to tell them that there continues to be an unsafe environment for urology patients here.'

There seems to be nothing more coveted or highly valued in the world of the NHS CEO than a good Care Quality Commission (CQC) rating and he looked angry as I left the room. Two days later, on the Sunday at 4 p.m., the Chief of Surgery phoned me.

'I've had (*the Chief Executive*) on the phone. He's very worried about what you said.'

'Good,' I said. 'He should be,' and, at her request, ran through the story a third time.

'Gosh, it sounds serious,' she said.

This was frustrating to say the least because she must have been well aware of the seriousness of the situation by the numerous conversations she had had with me and others about this whole business going back some years now. The next morning, Monday, 2 December 2013, at 9 a.m., the Chief Executive phoned me and asked if I meant what I had said on Friday.

'Yes, of course I do,' I replied.

'Well, I need it in writing.'

And with that the call ended. He phoned again at lunchtime; his tone more aggressive. 'Where is it? I haven't received anything yet.'

'I've been in clinic seeing patients all morning but will get it to you this afternoon.'

I left clinic, went to my office, opened the computer and typed up one side of A4, summarising the care this man had received and pointing out where there were shortcomings. I put in a title "Expression of concern over the management of patient (C)". I printed it off, took it up to the management offices and went into the Chief Executive's office.

Inside was the CEO, the Head of HR and a tense, tired-looking Medical Director. The Chief Executive took the piece of paper from me and gave it to the Medical Director, who pushed his up glasses and read the note from under the bottom of the rims. He then pushed a finger and thumb into his eyes and, nodding, gave it back to the CEO, who thrust it towards me, saying, 'Hang on, you haven't signed it.'

I duly signed it and gave it back.

The following day, Mr Miller was met at his clinic by the Medical Director and the Head of HR and was suspended. He was instructed not to contact any patients or anyone from the Trust but, within two hours, had done both. I learned subsequently that he was told that he now had to agree to an investigation by the RCS, via the IRM process, or be referred to the GMC. Unsurprisingly, he agreed to the IRM.

On 31 December 2013, after more than seven years of raising concerns, the Medical Director wrote to the RCS formally asking them to investigate.

PART 3

Investigations

CHAPTER 1

Royal College of Surgeons' Investigation

THE INVITED REVIEW MECHANISM (IRM) is a service offered by the RCS which provides expert independent and objective advice to health care organisations. Its remit is to identify whether there is a basis for concerns raised about an individual surgeon or hospital practice, and to offer advice on how best to move forward. It was headed at that time by the late Miss (later Dame) Clare Marx, who was soon after made President of the RCS. The review takes the form of a visit by a panel of three, comprising two surgeons and one lay person, all trained to look at evidence put before them and to interview the individual concerned together with key witnesses, commonly other members of the department. It took some time for the Trust to arrange but a date was set for the beginning of April 2014.

In March, the CNSs, some of my colleagues and I were asked by the Medical Director to submit any evidence we wanted to be considered by the IRM panel. This was destined to be an important task requiring a great deal of thought and effort and I made some preliminary notes about how I might approach the issue, acutely aware that I did not have much time. Each working day was already very full and my anxiety levels were heightened a couple of weeks before the IRM visit when I was in Coroner's court in Woking for an unconnected case. The Chief of Surgery entered the courtroom and sat down next to me a few minutes after the case had started. She leaned over, gushing an apology that the parking had been terrible and, just before I was to take the stand, said, 'Oh, I meant to say, we've had the stuff through from Paul Miller for the IRM. There's mountains of it. Boxes and boxes.'

The next day, I asked to see the boxes – all six of them crammed with files and records of meetings, emails, printed notes and, oddly, a list of "trial patients". I started going through them early one evening with Kate and Catherine after clinic. A couple of hours into it, we came across a piece of paper, which purported to be a typed note to one of them regarding patient C, the key patient which had led to his most recent suspension. We doubted the authenticity of the note – to our knowledge he had never sent a typed note to the nurses like this before, and its contents seemed to confirm that it had been constructed to mislead the investigators.

We were discussing what we could do about it – if anything – when in the next box file we came across something more unsettling and upsetting. It was a signed statement from the previous Chief of Surgery who had been my main point of contact in the early years of raising concerns. In our numerous meetings he had assured me repeatedly that he was aware of the problem and that the hospital was looking into the issue. It was he who had assured me that the hospital was looking at dismissing Mr Miller, apparently not even bothering too much about the possible costs of being found guilty of unlawful dismissal – 'Cheap at the price,' he had said, on more than one occasion. He had written to Mr Miller regarding the concerns that I had raised and was aware of the restrictions placed on his practice. Furthermore, it was he who had written to Mr Miller requesting him (too politely in my view) to comply with the restrictions placed on his practice.

What would he write in his statement to the RCS? I started reading it and quickly came across so many falsehoods that I assumed there had been a mix-up and that the statement applied to someone else. I repeatedly checked the names, looking for evidence that there had been an error but sadly there wasn't. I found it difficult to take my eyes off one paragraph in particular, which started, "I was not aware of any clinical concerns about Mr Miller's practice when I was Chief of Surgery and I am surprised that they are being raised now".

I felt utterly betrayed by the hospital management. 'At least he is no longer Chief,' I said out loud. But it made us think: if at least one manager was simply going to deny it all, what other surprises might there be in store for us? What would he and the other managers say when interviewed? Particularly now that some of the material put before the IRM panel by Mr Miller appeared to have been fabricated, I was concerned that this could very easily all go horribly wrong. If the RCS were to investigate and not find too much wrong then that would be the end of the matter and all the problems would continue. And where would that leave me? I wondered.

We chatted as we continued to go through the material. What should we be submitting to the IRM panel, and how? We of course had a duty to state our concerns but what we uncovered in the material submitted by Mr Miller had spooked me. The evidence of duplicity and denial from the management and fabrication from Mr Miller raised in my mind the concern that it might all descend into a he said-she said series of arguments. Additionally, our allegations of improper actions by Mr Miller risked feeding into his narrative of being a victim of personal opposition to him rather than legitimate concerns over patient care. We discussed it among ourselves, not knowing what the right thing to do would be. We couldn't ask the management for help or advice – they had been of precisely no help up to this point and now a senior manager had flatly denied any knowledge of a problem at all.

Going through all the boxes of material we had been given was laborious and time-consuming and, with just ten days to go, we seemed to be running out of time and started sandwiching our preparation between clinics or theatre and working into the evenings. Patient letters had to be checked on the hospital's hard drive, the various claims in the documentation had to be researched and clinical notes had to be retrieved and examined. Knowing that anything submitted would be seen by all parties, and now aware of the tactics the managers and Mr Miller were content to employ, we concluded that the best plan would be to submit a list of patients about whom we were concerned and concentrate the remaining time on assembling evidence to counter Mr Miller's and the managers' evidence. We just hoped that that, together with an in-depth knowledge of the cases we would ask them to look at, would be sufficient to demonstrate our concerns.

There were a number of disadvantages with this approach. One was that, although each of us had some patients we could remember, none of us would have come across them all, let alone kept a list of them. Another worry was that a superficial reading of any individual patient's notes was far from guaranteed to reveal deficient care: the management plan was not always recorded in the patients' notes, which themselves were sometimes incomplete and didn't always accurately reflect the consultation that had taken place. Even reading the typed letter sent out following a consultation could be misleading because Mr Miller's patients were frequently not copied into the correspondence following their outpatient appointment, making inconsistencies between what was said in clinic and what appeared in the letter difficult to identify. Taken in the round, this all meant that even the most diligent and conscientious review of the notes might fail to uncover what had been going on.

We each wrote a list of patients we could recall having concerns about, and cross referencing them quite quickly got to more than fifty between us. We explained our strategy to the Medical Director and forwarded the names and hospital numbers of the patients we wanted reviewed. The list was forwarded to medical records and we awaited the delivery of the fifty sets of patient notes so that we could begin studying them and making summaries of the key milestones in their treatment, clearly identifying along the way the concerns we had.

Unfortunately, the message soon came back that over half the sets of notes could not be located. It emerged that some were known to be sitting in a distant off-site storage facility, some were incomplete with missing volumes and many had been tracked to various clinics and wards in the hospital but just could not be found. With the recent insight into how Mr Miller and the management would behave, and now being faced with significant obstacles merely in getting hold of the majority of the notes we needed to scrutinise, we really seemed to be swimming a lonely course against a brisk current.

We toyed with the idea of trawling through the clinical letters on the urology department's hard drive to assemble new sets of notes, but not only would that be time-consuming, the information would necessarily be incomplete because we still wouldn't have the written record of consultations. Perhaps fifty was too many anyway, we wondered. We decided to settle on twenty that we knew the hospital had the notes for. The names would be submitted to the IRM, and Mr Miller, while being supervised, would have full access to them beforehand in a hospital office.

The fact that those carrying out the investigation would be a panel of skilled and experienced individuals underpinned by no less a body than the RCS meant that, whatever their conclusions, all concerned would be bound by it. If they were to report shortcomings in the management of patients, it would allow us to rectify such past errors and set them on the right treatment paths. But what would happen if they couldn't see what we could and came to what we would regard as the "wrong" conclusion?

•   •   •

Those of us who had been called to give evidence felt a great burden of responsibility and, as the visit drew closer, I became concerned that our strategy was wrong. Perhaps they wouldn't consider twenty patients enough to conclude this to be the large-scale, significant problem we judged it to be. Or what if, perhaps for the reasons above, the IRM panel simply couldn't see what we could? In the end, the lack of time forced our hand and we decided we must hold our nerve. We would provide the IRM panel with a list of patients about whose clinical management we had concerns, and I made it my business to understand precisely where I felt the standard of care had been unacceptably low. Additionally, we would spend time preparing a narrative to counter the material submitted by Mr Miller.

On that, and subsequent evenings, Lesley and I spoke about the IRM and the fact that the RCS might not be persuaded. What would we do? 'There's obviously no way I could continue to work there.'

Lesley agreed.

Having been responsible for raising concerns at the outset, and largely for driving the process forwards, if the one investigation that I had been insisting on for all these years – a proper, independent, external investigation – failed to show much, my position within the department and hospital would be untenable and I would have to leave. The trouble is that I was by now forty-eight years old with a mortgage and children in local schools.

'Where would we go?' I asked Lesley over another glass of wine.

'Far away.'

'Where?'

'Australia,' she replied.

I knew it made sense. I would make contact with my former colleagues to see if there was any opening in Queensland and as a family we would emigrate. It would mean having to do the Australi-an Urology board exams and it would be a big upheaval, but it would be for the best for everyone in the long run.

The panel's visit would last two or three days, we were told. On arrival at the hospital, they based themselves in an office in the management building and started their work. Towards the end of the first day, word came out that they had spent the whole time going through the submitted material from Mr Miller. They would next move on to the sets of patient notes and would be staying late into the evening before retiring to a local hotel. The next day, they interviewed Mr Miller for some hours. Surely this was a good sign, I thought. At least they appeared to be taking it seriously. But would they see what I and my colleagues could see?

The stakes could hardly have been higher the following day as I made my way into the hospital for my interview. I was happy with my preparation. I had studied the material in the box files thorough-ly, had made notes and had worked on responses to potential questions. I had also studied the case notes of the twenty patients we had asked to be looked at and made further notes on all of them.

At 9.30 a.m., I was collected from the waiting room, brought into the office and introduced to two Consultant Urological Surgeons: Mr Tim Terry, representing the RCS, and Mr Alan Paul, representing the British Association of Urological Surgeons; the lay member of the panel, Mrs Judith Worthington; and the note-keeper. I poured myself some water into the plastic cup in front of me and sat down, desperately wishing my heart would stop pounding.

I fished into my pocket, brought out my notes and, after the introductions, stated, 'Can I perhaps suggest I begin by going through the patients, pointing out where I feel their management might have been...'

'Don't worry.'

I looked up. 'What do you mean?' I asked.

'We get it,' Mr Terry replied.

'How do you mean, "you get it"?'

'What I mean to say', said Mr Terry, 'is that we can see these have all been mismanaged.'

It was now seven years since I had started raising concerns and, even in this meeting, my mind flicked back to some of the missed opportunities for the Trust to have acted sooner; many of the patients put before the IRM panel were the very same ones brought to the Trust's attention time and again over the previous years.

All the conversations with managers, the meetings, the passing on to them of patient notes, the detailed summaries given, the various reviews, and finally, *finally*, someone with the authority to look into it properly had come to the same conclusions held by my colleagues and me. The lack of sleep, the knowledge that I now wouldn't have to move job or consider emigrating, the sheer relief of hearing those words 'Don't worry, we get it' all conspired to make my mind go into a spin. I don't think I was much help to them during the interview but in a sense there was not much for me to say.

'He needs to be referred to the GMC, and the question is', Mr Terry went on, 'who should do the referring? It mustn't be you; it would make your life hell. It should be the Medical Director,' he concluded, adding that the panel would write to the hospital.

Shortly after the visit, on 7 April 2014, the Chair of the IRM, Miss Clare Marx, wrote to the Medical Director to give early feedback pending the submission of their final IRM report. The letter described the panel's significant concerns about what had been going on clinically but it also raised concerns about aspects of the Trust's handling of the issue, including of an SUI.

They were concerned that there were potentially large numbers of patients who had been put on "active surveillance" for prostate cancer or hormone treatment when they might have benefitted from a fuller consideration of other alternative treatments. They considered that Mr Miller's suspension should be continued and that all patients with a cancer diagnosis under his care going back to 2006 should now have an urgent Consultant review. They made it clear that this was an urgent patient safety issue, that immediate action was required by the Trust in relation to patient safety and that the Trust should contact the GMC.

Over the next few days, details emerged of the look-back exercise that the Trust now had to undertake. Although relieved by the RCS's conclusions, it was clear that this last instruction would be a monumental task: initial estimates were that there would be in excess of twelve hundred patients. Each of these would need to have their notes pulled from storage, some results would need to be looked up via the poorly functioning NHS IT systems, hard drives searched for additional letters, MDT sheets read and at times cross referenced to the MDT attendance log, the database of nurses' telephone conversations examined, handwriting in the clinical notes deciphered, etc.

But who should do the work? We were still in a sense recovering from the RCS's visit, and finding time to do a review of more than a thousand sets of notes while continuing a busy clinical job would be a challenge, to say the least. We discussed these issues with the Medical Director and concluded that realistically we were best placed to do it. Our knowledge of many of the patients and some of the idiosyncrasies of management were known to us, but would not be known to a third party. Additionally, trying to find someone else would inevitably impose a delay – and everyone now agreed that this was a pressing issue with patients potentially suffering more the longer it went on.

We therefore accepted the challenge and met to agree a way forward. The first step would be to compile a list of patients falling under the terms of the review. The CNSs Kate and Catherine were instrumental in compiling a database and requested for the notes to be delivered to the urology office. Within days, the whole of the urology office became swamped with hundreds of sets of patient notes. We took over the office next door and for many weeks there was box after box full of notes covering the entire floor and desk area of the two offices. We decided that the nurses would do an initial trawl of the notes and send back to storage all those with no management concerns. This would be the majority, and those where there were concerns were given to Abhay and me to look at. We went in at weekends and spent any spare time we had going through them, often together with the nurses to see what they thought too. Inevitably, some notes didn't come, some were incomplete and some were difficult to be sure about, but we whittled it down to a list of about a hundred cases that we judged to have been mismanaged.

These would now need to be assessed in more detail. Abhay and I were very keen not to be involved in the final judgment and NHS England came up with the terms and structure of an external review panel comprising a Consultant Urologist from outside the cancer network, a CNS also from outside the region and a local senior GP was established. This Clinical Assessment Group (CAG), as it was named, would then put these patients into one of three categories – mismanaged and harmed, mismanaged but not harmed, or not mismanaged.

The CAG requested a summary of each patient, together with details of where we considered mismanagement to have occurred. This in itself was a huge task because it would entail further scrutiny of the one hundred sets of patient notes and writing a summary for each from referral, through diagnosis to discussion of management options and treatment given. There then needed to follow a list of concerns regarding management, together with explanations. By using free, personal time, including much annual leave, I managed to write the overwhelming majority of them.

As the results started to filter back from the panel, it was clear that they agreed that most had been mismanaged, with many patients sadly suffering harm as a consequence. All of these patients then needed to be discussed at the MDT and seen in clinic to explain what had happened. Up-to-date imaging or biopsies frequently needed to be carried out; the results of which would then need to go back to MDT to be discussed again and a management plan devised. The patient would then need to be seen once more in clinic to put them on a correct treatment pathway. All of this meant a great deal more work for me and the wider team, and we set up a series of additional clinics to see them, using time normally set aside for admin.

On being told that they had been judged to have been mismanaged, patients' reactions varied a great deal but most were just grateful for getting on to the right track. Some had clearly suffered as a result – either the side effects of inappropriate treatment or progression of disease that might not have happened had they received the correct treatment from the outset. As we went through the list, it was clear that many had died. The hospital cross referenced these to the list of patients who had been determined to have been mismanaged by the CAG, and this resulted in ten patients being referred to the Coroner. I looked at the list with a sense of dread because, sadly, it contained some familiar names. Several on it featured in Philip Kemp's original look-back exercise of 2010.

While this new look-back exercise was happening, in May and June 2014 the Trust carried out an investigation into conduct issues to do with Mr Miller. The Trust emphasised that they wanted non-clinical reasons to dismiss him and I was asked to put in writing the fact that, on the day after there had been one of the blow-ups at the MDT, he had gone to Lord's to watch cricket.

Specifically, the issue concerned the occasion when Mr Miller had not wanted a patient seen in the bladder clinic at Guildford, saying he would instead see the patient himself. He was unable to see them the following day because he was going to watch cricket at Lord's and was then on annual leave for two weeks. The managers had discovered he had not applied for annual leave for that extra day and decided that they would use this as part of the evidence against him.

Despite everything that had happened, this made me feel distinctly uncomfortable. It was one thing raising concerns about patient safety but actively writing something about a relatively trivial incident was completely different, and I declined. The managers responded by repeating how important it was for them to have something in writing about conduct, and asked me again.

It really did seem ridiculous for them to be focusing on cricket and annual leave in the context of the hard-hitting RCS report, the large numbers of people who had been confirmed by the CAG to have been harmed and the ten deaths referred to the Coroner – and I wanted nothing to do with it. However, they were insistent, and so, towards the end of 2013, I agreed to be interviewed, but only on the basis that I could alter the transcript in any way I wanted so that I could be entirely happy with the wording.

I was duly interviewed by the Deputy Medical Director and subsequently spent considerable time agonising over the precise wording of the transcript, eventually coming up with a form of words I was content with. I explained that Mr Miller had not wanted the patient seen at Guildford and, right at the end of the statement, in response to being asked why he couldn't see him the following day, stated that, 'he couldn't as he was at the cricket on the Friday and I thought abroad after that, but that I couldn't be sure.' Little did I know then that these few words would subsequently be distorted and used as evidence against me by no less a figure than the Trust's Chief Executive.

The look-back exercise took months but we eventually completed it towards the end of the summer, and the CAG completed their assessment in September 2014. They set a high threshold, demanding clear, unambiguous, written evidence of mismanagement and harm, and found that sixty-five patients had been mismanaged and, of these, twenty-seven had been harmed as a consequence of the mismanagement. Ten of those had died and were referred to the Coroner.

The review of probity issues was completed and, in October 2014, Mr Miller was dismissed for gross misconduct by the Trust, which issued a press release the following week regarding the findings of the CAG.

We were given a few days' notice of this press release by the Medical Director. Inevitably, it would raise the anxiety levels of the local population and we felt that we needed to set up a helpline to field what we anticipated would be many calls from anxious patients and relatives. The CNSs were given a mobile phone and the number was publicised. As soon as the press release had concluded, the phone started ringing. The nurses took on most of this work and, despite not being given any training or advice, dealt with the callers with great professionalism, staying late into the evenings and taking the phone home at weekends.

This was a new experience to all of us and, although the RCS review had confirmed our fears and was undoubtedly a watershed moment in the whole story, it had nevertheless generated huge amounts of extra work. At times, it was harrowing listening to the plight of some of the patients, both on the telephone and in clinic, but the overriding emotions were of frustration and sadness at the fact that it all could – and should have – been sorted out years before. Nagging at the back of my mind was whether the Trust would face up to its failings and learn from its undoubted numerous, serious errors.

And I was determined to do everything I could to make sure that it did.

CHAPTER 2

GGI review

IN THE WEEKS FOLLOWING THE RCS REVIEW I cautiously enquired of the Medical Director why he thought the Trust hadn't acted sooner. He expressed what I judged to be a degree of personal upset over the issue, but it was troubling that there was no acknowledgement in our conversation of the significant failure at all levels of the Trust, including at the very top of the organisation, in the handling of this issue.

Discussions within the department with both medical and nursing colleagues confirmed that we shared an uneasiness that the Trust managers had got this whole issue very wrong from start to finish and yet there seemed no accountability. What we wanted was for the managers to face up to their shortcomings and to learn from their mistakes. I therefore started asking the Medical Director how the Trust intended to learn from its errors and suggested an external review into why action hadn't been taken sooner. He seemed unsure, or was perhaps wary, but after a while he agreed.

Perhaps true to form, nothing happened for some months and I wondered if he might have developed cold feet, but, at the end of 2014, the Medical Director fed back the findings of the CAG at a Consultant meeting in the Trust, and I grasped an opportunity in the questions section at the end of the talk to make my point to him.

'Clearly, something has gone very wrong here. You have previously given me a verbal undertaking that the Trust will investigate its actions in this matter but have not yet done so. Please can you confirm now that it will do so by commissioning an external review.'

Because he was speaking to an audience of the hospital's Consultants, he perhaps felt he had no real option but to agree. There then followed yet another delay, due, I am told, to the Trust having difficulties in finding a suitable company and agreeing terms. Eventually, the Trust commissioned the Good Governance Institute (GGI), an internationally recognised company specialising in reviews of the governance structure of large organisations, especially health care, to carry out the investigation, and they started in autumn 2015.

Their task would be to analyse evidence put before them and interview key members of staff to enable them to form conclusions about how the Trust had responded to concerns raised. Clearly, mistakes and delays had occurred but it remained to be seen whether they would find that the fault for this lay primarily at the hospital's door, as I and my colleagues felt was the case. Aware that the hospital managers would be robust in defending their actions, I invested considerable time and effort preparing for the visit, assembling documents, emails and contemporaneous notes I had made of various meetings and conversations, and I looked forward to my interview with a degree of confidence.

On 16 October 2015, I walked into the small office to a familiar scene – a recording device on a desk, the other side of which was a small team of investigators. I sat down and was introduced to the GGI's Chief Executive and the Senior Research and Development Officer.

'Okay, do you want to tell me what you see as the course of events here, Mr Swinn?' was the first question. The transcript shows that I stopped talking ninety-four minutes later, prompted here and there with a few questions but other than that I continued more or less uninterrupted.

There was a lot of head in hands and head shaking when I described what had happened, illustrating my points with the emails and notes in front of me. For the first time I had been able to tell the whole story from start to finish, and I found it a cathartic experience. It felt good to offload the frustrations of the previous eight years or so and, when I finished, although emotionally drained, I felt a considerable degree of relief. The interviews with colleagues in the urology department followed a similar pattern, and the list of those they sought to interview grew.

Given the scale and complexity of the issue, it took many months for them to complete their investigation and compile their report. I am told that concern from the Trust management about early drafts led to delays and it wasn't until late the following year that it was finalised. I had been tipped off that it wouldn't be pulling any punches and I remember the day it popped into my email inbox – all fifty-five pages of it, written in small type. It was titled "Investigation into the Surrey and Sussex Healthcare NHS Trust's response and governance procedures with regard to concerns raised around Mr Paul Miller's practice".

Once I started reading it that same evening I couldn't stop. As I ploughed on, late into the night, I mentally ticked off all the problems they identified with the Trust against a checklist I had and was pleased that they had pretty much got them all.

The GGI investigation team, the report explained at the outset, had followed standard NHS Root Cause Analysis methodology by establishing the chronology of events, highlighting key problems or failings along the chain of events, and for each key problem it identified contributory factors. They had interviewed more than fifty people, with each being interviewed by two GGI employees, and all transcripts were signed off by the interviewees.

The main conclusion that "the Trust missed crucial opportunities to act on concerns earlier" was simple, unequivocal and hard-hitting. Two particular missed opportunities were cited as Philip Kemp's pilot look-back exercise of 2010 and a failure to act on the verbal feedback from Professor Neal, the external expert reviewer, in 2011. The report concluded that, "Throughout the period under review the balance of decision making was weighted in favour of (protecting) a clinician's reputation and credibility rather than patient safety".

A grand total of eighteen key problems were identified, listed fully here, together with their main contributing factors:

1. Inadequate response to Mr Miller's failure to follow preferred referral pathways and MDT decisions.

The report commented that "even after nursing and medical staff escalated these issues, the Trust failed to tackle them effectively". It found that, while there were some appropriate initial efforts taken on behalf of the Trust's senior management to raise this with Mr Miller, no one took overall responsibility to ensure he changed his actions. The review concluded that "the issue of challenging a difficult and powerful personality outweighed concerns raised by a number of professionals and the Trust's failure to act early and appropriately encouraged his further non-compliance, with damaging consequences".

Among others, it found that weak leadership with a culture of lack of advocacy for patient safety were contributory factors.

2. Inadequate response to peer review criticisms about leadership and referrals.

There were regular peer reviews both internally and led by the cancer network. These reported on the failure to follow national referral guidelines. Unfortunately, the Trust did not act on them; its response with regard to peer review being branded "inadequate".

3. Lack of rigour and coordination around conflict-of-interest concerns.

The report commented that there appeared to be no clear engagement by executives in ensuring best value was achieved on investments in equipment by the Trust and poor control of the procurement process before 2011. This was compounded by a lack of confidence in how to handle concerns raised about conflict of interest. There was also, the report commented, a failure to ensure a new laser was used as intended, which may have had a direct clinical impact.

4. Lack of coordination of different concerns, complaints, investigations, etc.

The report found that "there was no Trust-led coordinated and patient-focused approach to patient safety, incident reporting and the sharing of information. This lack of process contributed to the failure to triangulate information between different incidents and to identify the common threads".

5. Failure by managers to follow up concerns and whistle-blowing process.

"This is one of the most notable early failures in the chain of events. While there is evidence throughout the period between 2008–2013 of management action following concerns raised, action is seen as variously late and inadequate, either in the strength of action taken or in the follow-up or closure of the issue.... with the effect that more patients were put at risk as a result."

The report identified many contributing factors, including the fact that no notes were taken from some early meetings where concerns were raised, that there was inadequate selection and support for clinical managers and an erroneous belief that concerns had to be put in writing. There was "a lack of patient focused culture and a culture of wishful thinking that the concerns raised were not true, or that things would improve".

6. Failure to follow the whistle-blowing process when first or second actions were unsuccessful.

Again, the report commented on weak clinical leadership within surgery and at board level, and it also described the anxiety among staff of possible repercussions of what they were doing. They also observed that "there was a lack of clarity in early versions of the whistle-blowing process (policy) about reporting lines other than via line management with no inclusion of a direct reporting route for raising concerns to a non-executive director".

7. Failure to require the second reviewer to report on Mr Miller's practice.

The report's authors found that "it is clear that the decision was made to invite the reviewer (Professor Neal) to look at the operations of the MDT rather than to specifically follow up concerns around Mr Miller's practice.... This represented a key failing in the chain of events as it paved the way for a critical missed opportunity to deal with these issues sooner".

As contributory factors to this failing, the report commented on reticence to challenge a clinician and also changes in senior leadership roles within the Trust, including at Medical Director level.

8. Elements of the investigation practice were inadequate.

The report found key problems with how the investigations were carried out. In fact, pretty much every aspect of carrying out an investigation was criticised, including the terms of reference, choice of reviewer and post investigation follow-up. They noted that "the terms of reference were problematic to the reviewers themselves.". The internal reviewer (Dr Lamb) "was not supported by specialist knowledge and thus felt inadequately equipped to challenge elements of practice reported in the investigation". And what actions were carried out after the various reviews? "The selection of recommendations to be implemented from the various reviews appears to be arbitrary at best and follow-up of implementation hard to trace".

9. Lack of feedback on investigations and incidents to staff.

The Trust's lack of a process for reporting back learning to those who had contributed to the various reviews was not only "a further cause of frustration to staff" but had important implications. "Its relevance as a key problem in the chain of events is that it illustrates another opportunity where connections, themes and inconsistencies might have been identified and the case could have been dealt with at an earlier stage".

10. Response to changes to clinical practice caused by Mr Miller's behaviour.

"The efforts of clinical staff to protect patients whom they believed to be at risk should be applauded. However, it appears that due to a lack of written evidence about Mr Miller's practice, the fact that they were violating professional codes (for example, diverting patients away from Mr Miller...) was the focus of senior response, rather than consideration of why they would take such a drastic step". The report cited, again, lack of focus on patient safety by the organisation as a key contributory factor.

11. Poor SUI and complaints processes including closing of the complaint (from Patient A) when it became an SUI and delays in completing report.

The authors criticised confusion around the nature of review 1 (the "Lamb report"), the fact that the SUI was simply closed and the "considerable delays" to completing the SUI report. Again, a key contributing factor was that "the Trust's culture at the time was not primarily focused on patients and ensuring their safety".

12. Failure to act on the Surgery Divisional Chief Nurse's look-back report and recommendations.

The GGI report made the observation that the Kemp report made recommendations that mirrored the RCS's conclusions three and a half years later and, had it been heeded, "could potentially have brought matters to a head three years earlier in 2010". The report found that the focus (of the Trust) was on the potential threat to a clinician's reputation and repercussions from challenging him. They also commented on the high rate of churn in staff roles in the Trust's senior management at the time, which they felt also contributed to the failings.

13. Acceptance of poor Consultant attendance and behaviour; lack of appraisals and job planning process.

The report described inadequate management of Consultants' behaviour in the early stages of raising concerns with weak leadership contributing to the issue.

14. Board not sighted to key issues relating to Mr Miller in a timely manner.

The GGI found that the first official report of the case to the Trust board occurred just before the IRM visit during a private session of the board and pointed out that, of the several routes that could have been used to draw it to their attention earlier, none were used. They found evidence of non-executive members asking for more information about serious incidents and "while it cannot be claimed that earlier notification would have changed the outcome for patients and staff, this does suggest a culture where the value and purpose of a unitary board may not have been fully realised and understood".

15. Reviewer 2's (the external expert, Professor Neal's) verbal feedback of mismanagement of patients was not acted upon.

The report comments that "this is the second point in the chain of events where an opportunity to act at an earlier time was missed. The terms of reference for this review required a view on the working of the urology MDT rather than a view on Mr Miller's practice. However, it is reported that Reviewer 2 fed back verbally to the CEO his substantial concerns around Mr Miller's management of patients". The report referred to the red folder which Reviewer 2 had been given by the nurses, and made the following comments: "There are 39 instances of brief annotations concerning clinical care and management… It is our view that these do constitute the expression of concerns on the part of the expert involved and would support the assertion made by interviewees that Reviewer 2 expressed concerns verbally".

16. Failure to adequately measure and discuss clinical outcomes within the urology service.

"There does not appear to have been a rigorous process to triangulate areas of concern raised by audit, incidents or complaints with examination of clinical data". The contributory factors identified were underdeveloped clinical governance processes and a failure to triangulate data due to inadequate IT and data analysis support.

17. Senior Independent Director (SID) not notified of concerns.

Contributory factors to this were that the whistle-blowing policy was not well understood or communicated and that the SID role within the Trust was not supported.

18. Failure to secure and act on clinical opinion in patient A (first SUI) case.

Again, the issue of lack of clarity of the investigation's terms of reference and failure to keep to timescales were judged to have contributed to this failure.

The report went on to describe the main themes it had identified. These related primarily to the Trust's culture and systems. The culture, they concluded, was not in the least bit encouraging of the raising of concerns: "Staff who reported concerns have been clear to the review team that they were at times made to feel disapproved of by senior staff as though they were meddling in other people's lives (meaning Mr Miller's) ... Many staff also reported a fear for the security of their jobs if they were seen to be 'making waves'".

Nor were the managers au fait with the correct processes in such cases: "There was a widespread belief amongst senior staff that there was a requirement for concerns to be raised only in writing if they were to be actioned, even though written policies did not require this directly or implicitly".

The GGI report concluded that, due to a number of interconnected reasons, "the Trust missed crucial opportunities to act on concerns raised by a number of staff. Amongst many contributing factors, there were both cultural and systems issues. A reluctance to address concerns that could affect a clinician's reputation, poorly developed reporting, assurance systems and professional leadership have been identified as key determinants that had led to appropriate action not being taken at an earlier stage".

•   •   •

I finished reading, wondering what the impact of such a clear and damning report would be. I felt for the patients and their relatives and imagined their rising anger as it dawned on them that much misery could have been spared if only appropriate action had been taken earlier. I also wondered whether it would affect my relationship with the Trust.

Within a few days, I was invited to a meeting with the Medical Director and senior representatives from the GGI, including Professor Corbett-Nolan, the CEO who had interviewed me many months before. They presented the report and key findings to a more or less silent and depressed-looking Trust senior management team. It was clear that the report would make troubling reading to those who had suffered, and the release of it would have to be delicately handled.

The hospital decided to be proactive and to present the findings to invited relevant parties. It would invite all patients deemed to have been mismanaged, together with a friend or relative. I was asked to go along to help with any clinical questions that might arise at the end. I felt that this was a sensible way of dealing with it, because at least the Trust management could deal directly with the inevitable fallout, and the CNSs and I would be on hand to help support patients and do our best to answer any clinical questions. A date was fixed, 30 September 2016, and invitations sent. As it turned out, so many people accepted the invitation that the hospital could not comfortably accommodate them all in one place at one time and so it was decided to carry it out in two identical seminars on the same afternoon.

On the day in question, I was sitting in the lecture hall as it started to fill with dozens of patients and relatives. They filed in silently and, although none of them knew for sure what to expect, the grim expressions on their faces suggested that they had more than an inkling of what was in store. The Chief Executive and other Trust managers were seated on stage behind a long table and, after sound system checks were completed, welcomes and introductions were made.

There was a tense, uneasy atmosphere in the lecture theatre as the presentation started. I was just thinking how glad I was not to be on stage when I saw the Chief Executive frantically looking round the lecture theatre. He caught my eye and gestured for me to come up on stage and join him. I was reluctant and I put up my hand to indicate that I was happy where I was. But he gestured again with a degree of impatience or perhaps anger, and so I reluctantly got up and made my way to the stage where space was made for me to sit alongside him.

I had been led to believe that the meeting had been convened by the hospital's senior management to apologise to people who had been medically mismanaged, explain that the hospital had made a series of errors in dealing with this issue and to reassure them that changes had or would be made. While, in fairness, the managers did state that they could have acted sooner, in the tone of the presentation and what was said, an entirely unwarranted and misleading message was also being communicated to the audience.

That message was that the urology department was responsible for the harm done – not an individual within it or the managers for failing to act sooner but the urology department itself. The poor outcomes that patients had endured were emphatically not of my making and being made to sit alongside the very managers who had got it so wrong for so long and to whom I had raised concerns repeatedly was very unfair. It seemed very much that they were keen to have me there sitting alongside them sharing the blame and apologising together.

The silence during the presentation was replaced by anger at its conclusion. Once the penny had dropped with those in the audience that their complications, disease progression or perhaps relative's death were for the most part entirely avoidable, the object of their ire, as far as they were concerned, was right before them on stage.

When I first read the GGI report I wondered what effect it might have on my relationship with the Trust.

I was beginning to find out.

CHAPTER 3

Coroner's inquests

HER MAJESTY'S CORONER was notified of the ten deaths among those deemed to have been mismanaged and soon after came her decision to carry out inquests into all of them.

Many pre-inquest hearings were scheduled in order to establish some of the logistical arrangements of the hearings, including timings. Several were cancelled at short notice due to ill health. This must have been immensely frustrating for the families and it was also problematic for those of us involved. Eventually, a date was set by the Coroner to hear all ten over a period of a few weeks in April and May 2018. I cleared my diary, noting that it would clash with the family Easter holiday, which we would have to postpone.

At the final pre-inquest hearing on 14 March 2018, various issues were discussed, including details of the witness list, but, irritatingly, a decision was made to postpone the hearing yet again and new dates were issued for it to take place on various days between 21 May and 27 July 2018.

I gave my availability, clinical activity was cancelled and a pre-inquest in-house meeting at the hospital was set up for 14 May 2018. Frustratingly, with just days to go, the Coroner stated that she had decided that "with the clear issues of commonality running through these cases it must be right to hear all these cases together", and with that the hearings were postponed again to a new start date of 8 October 2018.

On 24 September 2018, I met with the Trust lawyers, Capsticks. I had been slightly put off by the email I had received setting up the meeting to which the Medical Director and I were both invited because it referred to the "division of labour" between us. I was prepared to answer questions about what I knew, and when, and what I had done to raise concerns. But talk of a division of labour between me and the Medical Director suggested that we had a job of work to do together, and I was not at all sure that I knew what they meant by that.

When I arrived, the Medical Director was already there, looking stressed and unhappy, making me wonder about the nature of the conversation he had just had with the Capsticks lawyers. He finished talking to them soon after I arrived and left. The meeting was recorded and the transcript shows what I was told to expect about my time on the witness stand: "The primary purpose of calling you is to talk through the precis, (to give) the Trust's story and give counter-balance to Mr Miller's story ...so you need to be prepared and swat up on the precis and overview of each of those patients and in particular decisions made (by the) MDT. (We) will make sure you have got any relevant documents you would like to see".

I suddenly felt very uneasy indeed. Surely it was not up to me to defend the Trust – "to give the Trust's story" – as they put it. To do that would mean taking on Mr Miller and his legal team. I was merely being called as a witness, and the thought of being cross-examined by goodness knows how many barristers was unappealing, to say the least, especially as the remit I was being given was to defend the Trust, when in reality I was highly critical of their handling of the whole affair over many years. Surely it was up to the Medical Director of the Trust during his time on the stand to defend his and his Trust's handling of the affair?

My anxiety levels were raised further over the next few days when the Trust emailed me, saying I "had to" attach all the precis of the ten patients to my statement. This meant it would be me personally entering the material before the court, leaving me open to cross-examination and challenge on the content. And all this despite the fact that only one of them had ever been my patient. I quickly took some informal legal advice from a friend who is a criminal defence barrister.

His advice was crystal clear. I should not be responsible for submitting the precis – that was the job of the Medical Director – and, moreover, I should not be pressurised into so doing. I therefore politely, but very clearly, declined their directive to attach them to my witness statement. The response I got from the Trust seemed entirely unreasonable. In two further emails in rapid succession, they stated that I "need" to attach them, and that I "must" attach them.

If they were right that the precis had to be entered into court by an individual, surely the Medical Director should be responsible? I had been asked to write patient summaries for the CAG and had done so in good faith, but they were never intended to form part of a witness statement. They belonged to the hospital and should be entered into court by the hospital or its senior managers.

It concerned me that they were so keen for the Medical Director not to be the one entering them into court, and I suspected they knew that whoever did would be given a lengthy and uncomfortable time on the witness stand, cross-examined by multiple barristers and all in full glare of the national press. The precis had been written years before, not all of them had been written by me, and yet here I found myself with just a few days to go before the start of the hearings, trying my best to rebuff attempts by managers to make me take centre stage and become the focal point for cross-examination.

An additional key concern I had was that, despite asking for it repeatedly, the Trust had not shown me Mr Miller's statement. I was finally given it on Friday 28 September 2018, just a few days before taking the stand. It was dated March 2017 and it subsequently turned out that it had been in the hospital's possession for many months. It was a very lengthy document with many appendices, and I started reading it between operations. Before long, my eyes fell on a letter purporting to be from Mr Miller to patient C and copied to me. Its contents referred to a clinical aspect of treatment for his bladder cancer which had, in fact, been settled some months before the date of the letter, and it implied the patient had declined a cystectomy. I had never seen the letter before and to my mind it was clearly a fake, yet, if the Coroner accepted it at face value, it would be interpreted as evidence supporting Mr Miller's case.

I had previously analysed patient C's case thoroughly and I knew it not to be in the notes and concluded that it must have been fabricated. I showed it to Marion, one of the urology secretaries, and asked her to look into it. Ten minutes later, she knocked on my open door.

'Well, it hasn't come from here,' she confirmed. 'The font is wrong, the "private and confidential" is written in the wrong place and there is no record of it on the hard drive.'

It clearly had been concocted and, knowing submitting a falsified document before a Coroner to be a serious issue, I raised it immediately with the Medical Director and explained my reasoning for concluding that the letter was forged.

"Surely this is perverting the course of justice," I wrote to the Medical Director, and suggested the Coroner be notified, or perhaps even the police. The Trust's Head of Legal Affairs was not contactable and the Medical Director's response to me by text didn't fill me with confidence: "I couldn't see his (Mr Miller's) statement in my witness bundle and I'm not in today…"

In the days that followed it was clear that neither he nor the Trust's legal team were keen to challenge it. I insisted on a meeting with Mr Robert Cohen, Counsel for the Trust, who explained his view that the Coroner's inquest was not the right time to raise the issue. But I was not convinced. Surely the Coroner should know that she was being presented with evidence which seemed so clearly to have been invented?

The following Friday, 5 October, again while trying to do an operating list, I was asked up to the Trust's legal office to sign my statement. I was about to sign it when I saw that, despite me being repeatedly and explicitly clear that I wasn't going to attach any precis, the Trust was intending to do exactly that.

I therefore refused to sign it until they confirmed that they would not be attached. The Head of Legal Services seemed uncertain what to do and suggested I go and see the Chief Executive, and I headed towards his office. As I entered, I was immediately confronted by anger – he had been made aware that I hadn't signed my statement. I stood my ground, reiterating my reason for not having done so, but he became yet more angry with a raised voice and jabbing his finger at me. I blurted out my reasoning again for not having signed it and added that this whole business had now been going on for many years, during which time the Trust had essentially done nothing right and had shown no thought of how difficult it had been for those of us involved. I muttered something about needing a break and left his office.

Within the hour, a senior Trust manager phoned me and berated me for the full duration of the call, which my phone records show lasted fourteen minutes. My contemporaneous notes record her repeatedly telling me I 'had to attach the precis to my statement.' I gave a logical, cogent explanation as to why I wouldn't and countered that they should come from the Trust.

But she persisted. 'We really need you to do this, Mike.'

When I continued to hold my ground, she said, 'Just to be clear, are you definitely saying you won't do it? If so, the case will collapse.'

I told her again that the Medical Director should be the one to put it officially before the court, and the expert witnesses (several had been called by the Coroner) would be on hand to answer any urological questions if required and I could help with specifics of the cases.

There was a long pause at this point and then she said, '(*The Medical Director*) is not available to go to court.'

'What! Why?'

'Er, family issues.'

I was incredulous and felt ever more like a lamb being thrown before a pride of hungry lions. It became clearer to me why the hospital did not want the Medical Director to enter them into court – he was not even going to be there, leaving me as the most senior employee of the Trust for the duration of the hearings!

Despite my repeated protestations, the Trust continued to harass me all day but I argued repeatedly for the precis to be entered into court under the Medical Director's name, even if he wasn't going to attend. Finally, during the evening of that same day, Friday, 5

October, with the inquests starting first thing on Monday morning, the Trust emailed me, conceding that I did not have to.

When I enquired what solution they had come up with, I was informed that the precis had been entered into court previously at one of the pre-inquest review meetings. It was therefore clear that their repeated haranguing of me, including threats of me being responsible for the collapse of the hearings, were not only grotesquely unfair and unwarranted, they were also entirely misplaced in terms of legal process.

Needless to say, this episode was profoundly upsetting, but I could not afford to let it unsettle me because I needed to spend the weekend preparing for my time on the stand the following week. One consolation was that I knew that Kate and Catherine would be going through a similarly anxious time and we were able to keep each other level-headed. Abhay had a long-standing meeting abroad and would not be taking the stand. On the Monday morning, Kate, Catherine and I met early and went into Coroner's court together, doing our best to dodge the press photographers. We sat together at the back in seats, it turned out, we would occupy for the duration.

It was difficult watching Kate and Catherine give their evidence. They were very eloquent but it was clearly difficult and emotional recounting events, including their repeated pleas for the hospital to listen to them.

The court rose to break for lunch.

'And when we return, we will hear from Mr Swinn,' the Coroner said.

As I stood up to leave the room, I bumped into the widow of patient C. She asked me if I had spotted in the legal bundle of papers the letter from Mr Miller which I believed to have been fabricated. She had come across it and had come to the same conclusion. I told her that the Trust and their legal team had refused to have anything to do with it and there was a risk that it might be accepted by the Coroner.

'I've got an idea,' she said. 'Why don't I get Clodagh (her QC) to ask you about it?'

It was a kind offer and a sensible solution because it meant that I could get across my evidence for the letter being forged, and it would also mean that other people would, in time, be questioned on it.

I was desperately trying to keep calm as I took to the stand to be cross-examined by four QCs and the Coroner. I was asked why I thought patient management had been poor and what I had done to address the situation, and I managed to get across pretty much all the points I wanted to, including the letter, which Clodagh Bradley QC did indeed ask me about in detail. All went according to plan, and at the end of a long line of questioning from the QC of one of the families, I was asked to summarise what it was like raising concerns for all those years.

The next day, several newspapers carried the story – and my response to that last question. One carried the headline "Coroner accuses hospital consultant, 60, of going on a 'jolly' by using his own experimental treatment on 10 patients who later died". It went on: "Doctors and nurses repeatedly blew the whistle as early as 2007. One senior consultant, Michael Swinn, said he had 20 to 30 meetings raising concerns about Mr Miller's care and even took his complaints directly to the Trust's chief executive. The journalist added, quoting me from court: "It was like hitting your head against a brick wall. It hurts and it doesn't achieve anything."

The Coroner's court was not finished though. When the expert witnesses took the stand, they were asked what they thought were the chances of patient C being cured, had MDT advice been followed. Tragically, they thought about a ninety-five per cent probability. That, and the clear way in which the Trust's inaction was presented by multiple witnesses, conspired to make it a very bad first week for the Trust. The question was, what would the managers do about it?

The Chief Executive phoned me on the Sunday, 14 October, at 4 p.m. He started by explaining that the Medical Director would be unavailable for the inquests at any point. and went on to say that he had been asked by the Coroner to take the stand but had declined to do so. He went on to say that the Trust had written to the Head of the Coroner service asking for the current Coroner to recuse herself. I hadn't heard that word before and sought clarification from him.

'We are trying to get a different Coroner.'

My heart sank. They seemed to be trying to put a halt to proceedings, and my instincts were proved correct when the following week the inquests were adjourned. 'I'm sorry', we were told, 'but it looks like you're all going to have to do it again next year.'

Within weeks of the inquests being adjourned, information started filtering through to me of a change in the hospital's approach.

'They're terrified of a corporate manslaughter charge,' I was told by a senior manager at the heart of the Trust, whose patience with her colleagues had clearly worn thin. 'It might even be that they are held personally accountable,' she continued. 'Their strategy is basically going to be that they couldn't have acted sooner as you didn't give them enough to go on.'

These words made me shudder and feel even more vulnerable. I thought of all the times evidence had been presented to them – the Kemp report, the Lamb report, the numerous sets of notes with a precis stapled to the front, Professor Neal's feedback, including his annotations on the twenty-six patients in the red folder, the inconsistencies that arose from the SUIs and, of course, the GGI report. I just hoped that all this would come out in Coroner's court under cross-examination. If it didn't, then there was a real risk that I and my colleagues would come out of this process badly.

Initial talk of the inquests being rescheduled for January came to nought and, when they were rescheduled for July 2019, the prospect of a further six-month delay made me even more fed up. The change in attitude of the senior management team towards me that I had detected with the publication of the GGI report, and which was crystallised at the Coroner's inquests, continued. I experienced varying reactions when seeing them out and about in the hospital; most commonly being blanked by them. When catching their eye, they seemed to have a sudden need to walk off in the opposite direction or perhaps become engrossed by their mobile phones.

I seemed very much on the outside, with no means of support in the hospital, and this sense of isolation, together with the interminable dragging on of this issue, was very subduing. It was sucking up ever more time and I felt helpless because the Trust, aided by their legal team, dictated events over which I had no control. It was extracting an ever-greater cost to me professionally and personally, and the souring of relationships with senior Trust managers contributed to the difficulties.

I sought informal advice from a lawyer friend of mine, who advised me that I put in a formal grievance and submit papers to an employment tribunal. I next took formal legal advice from a lawyer specialising in employment issues. The advice was identical. 'How on earth can you work there?' she asked me at the end of our first meeting.

I could not go on like this and decided that I would have to leave, and so made an appointment to see the Chief Executive. When we met in his office one dark afternoon in December 2018, I pointed out how poorly the hospital had handled this whole affair, that it had had a significant impact on me and my family, that the hospital's failure to act in a timely manner had contributed to this and how it had treated me so unfairly in the run-up to the Coroner's inquests.

I also wanted reassurance from the Trust that, if faced with a similar problem in the future, it would act differently, both in terms of its actions to tackle poorly performing doctors and in its behaviour towards those raising concerns. Unfortunately, my statement served to enrage him and he repeatedly stated how well the Trust had treated me. 'I've got loads of evidence that we have treated you very well, Mr Swinn,' he said while gesturing towards his bookshelf behind him, which I noticed was oddly empty.

I said that the Trust appeared to have shifted its position from previously accepting its failings in these matters to now seeking to push the blame for not acting sooner on to those of us who did all we could to raise concerns. I said that I was now in a position where I felt I needed to defend myself while, in fact, all I had done was raise concerns about patient safety; something I had a duty to do and that I and my colleagues had done repeatedly.

'Well, get your defence organisation then,' he snapped loudly while, not for the first time, jabbing a finger at me.

I pointed out that I had already contacted my defence organisa- tion (a legal service which I paid for personally to indemnify me in private practice), who were clear that they would not represent me for an NHS issue. It was a surreal and deeply upsetting experience with no hint of insight by the Chief Executive about what I and my colleagues had been through, nor any apparent acceptance of the need for change in the organisation. Two weeks later, in January 2019, the letter I received from a member of the Trust board did nothing to reassure me:

"It should be noted that the Trust is confident that at all times it did what it could to address the concerns raised about Paul Miller based on the evidence and information that was available at the time. Once evidence was available that supported allegations of improper behaviour by Mr Miller, action was taken very swiftly by the Trust. In respect of Mr Swinn's request for … confirmation that it would act differently in the future if faced with the same circumstances, whilst the Trust acknowledges current challenges caused by the situation involving Paul Miller, it does not consider that it acted improperly or inappropriately at any stage".

All my suspicions, it seemed, were confirmed and I was feeling ever more uncomfortably squashed between the Trust and their legal team on one side and by Mr Miller and his legal team on the other.

Concluding that the Chief Executive was too invested in the situation to see straight, I decided that a more independent view was warranted from a non-executive director.

The Trust board was identical in structure and function to that across many large organisations inside and outside the NHS, comprising executive and non-executive directors – with the latter having the responsibility and power to challenge decisions made by the executive team. I therefore made an appointment to see the Senior Independent Director (SID) of the Trust and we met on 7 February 2019. She kindly gave me a bottle of water as I settled into my seat and I told her the whole story from start to finish. She was unaware of the GGI report, which I urged her to read. As the story unfolded, she was clearly shocked and seemed sympathetic. I said that what I wanted was some sort of acknowledgement from the Trust that they had got an awful lot wrong and a commitment that they would put in place some changes to make sure that they would handle things better if confronted with a similar situation in the future. After an hour and a half, the meeting finished with her offering to do some finding out after which we would meet up again.

I felt encouraged that she had listened to me. I was sure she had taken on board my story and I looked forward to meeting up with her again. I could envisage, perhaps, working with her to come up with some new policies for the hospital and it was therefore with some optimism that I went back to see her two weeks later. I was sure there would be an apology and probably some ideas for change, and thought it would be a good opportunity for Lesley to hear directly from her and so I asked her to come along with me to the meeting.

It never ceases to amaze me how much can be deduced just from assessing another's body language; perhaps it was the lack of eye contact or the way she was turned slightly away from us, but I knew as soon as Lesley and I entered the room that something was wrong.

'Okay,' she began, 'I have been doing some finding out and the thing is that when we say something to other people, sometimes we think we are getting a message across when in fact we aren't?'

I stopped to take this in.

She was basically saying that I hadn't made myself clear enough when I was raising concerns.

All I could do was laugh.

'Who have you been talking to?' I asked. 'No, let me guess. The CEO?'

She nodded.

'Anyone else?'

'No.'

'Are you seriously saying that you believe that all the evidence the hospital had was not enough?'

I looked across at Lesley and was desperately saddened to see her crying, head in hands.

I had expected a non-executive director to be independent-minded from the executive but, as it turned out, she had discussed the matter with only one person, the Chief Executive, and was now seemingly parroting the party line that we had not done enough in raising concerns about Mr Miller.

I was incredulous and I felt so sorry for Lesley, who had come along with the expectation that something positive would come out of the meeting, including perhaps some concrete steps to bring about change. Neither of us had foreseen how ineffectual the SID would be. There was not much more to say and, as we got up to go, I asked her if she had read the GGI report. She hadn't.

Two weeks later, on 5 March 2019, I arrived at work early in the morning to do my cancer clinic and found a letter on my desk.

"By hand" was written on the envelope. "Personal – to be opened by Mr Swinn only".

I opened it and read, open-mouthed, and with mounting anger: "In the circumstances it would not be appropriate for Capsticks to continue to support you in our role as the Trust's solicitors and counsel and I suggest you seek advice from your medical defence organisation".

The Trust was removing all legal support for me. I had now been cut further adrift because not only did I not have the support of the senior management of the hospital, nor that of the non-executives, I had now also lost legal support. This meant that I would be subjected to cross-examination without a lawyer present and that I would have no means of questioning what was said in court by others.

I did not realise it immediately but it also meant that I would not have access to the legal bundle – the documents pertaining to the inquests, including the witness statements of the Chief Executive and the Medical Director. The suggestion in the letter that I seek advice from my medical defence organisation was, of course, disingenuous, because I had already made it clear that I had contacted them and had obtained the unambiguous response that my professional indemnity covered private practice only and therefore was not of use here.

I asked my lawyer (whose regular invoices had by now alarmingly totalled in excess of £20,000) to provide an estimate of the costs involved in having a barrister to accompany me through the hearing. She duly sent through a list of suitable people, together with their hourly rates. A quick back-of-the-envelope calculation suggested that the cost to me personally would be several tens of thousands of pounds. Such a sum was entirely unaffordable and I decided that I would have to go without.

Now that I had no legal representative, I decided that I should attend the pre-inquest hearing on 3 May 2019, and took some annual leave to do so. I sat at the back and awkwardly nodded a hello to the Trust's team of lawyers, noting that it had been beefed up from the original inquests the year before. They had recruited Anne Studd QC, a highly ranked and experienced senior barrister, and she sat with the Trust's Head of Legal Services and Robert Cohen, who had represented the Trust the previous year. They occupied a couple of desks in a line with many others at which the legal teams of other interested parties sat, including the team from the Spire Hospital Group and families of the bereaved.

As proceedings started, the Trust's legal team attracted the Coroner's attention to my presence and I was asked to move to a desk in line with everyone else's. I was asked by the Coroner directly about my status and had to reply that I did not know what she meant by that term. Fierce debate then took place, with various legal teams interjecting with their own views.

Although the pre-inquest hearing was being held principally in order to determine the practicalities of the inquest – when it would be heard, what witnesses would be called, etc. – it was in reality a hugely adversarial affair with legal teams doing their best to score points or gain the upper hand in some way. After a while, it was decided that I would continue as a witness, at which point Mr Miller's barrister stood up, made eye contact with me and with a menacing tone declared himself as relishing the opportunity to cross-examine me in due course. I sat there alone, feeling small, as the bickering between the parties continued; my lack of legal representation inducing more than a little anxiety.

It proved difficult to relax during a short family summer holiday in Scotland before the inquests started at the end of September, with an expected end date of 18 October 2019. I had been asked by the Coroner to keep much of the next few weeks free and, since I was not legally represented, made it my business to attend as much of the inquest as I could.

I managed to negotiate a slot on the witness stand towards the end of the hearing and, until then, occupied my customary position at the back of the courtroom where I could take notes unobserved. The Trust's Cancer Lead was called during the early stages and gave a detailed account of how he took on board the concerns that I and others raised with him and escalated those concerns to the Medical Director. 'My role carried no executive authority and I was therefore obliged to escalate all concerns to the management team.'

I wondered how the Medical Director would respond to that when he took the stand. There was just a short break before he was called. The room hushed as he took the oath and, speaking quietly, was asked repeatedly to speak louder. He was first asked about the handover from the outgoing Medical Director he had received on starting at the Trust, and replied that it had lasted an hour.

'You're telling me it was just one hour of a handover?' an incredulous Coroner asked.

The Kemp report came next.

'At what point did you look at the reports that had already been obtained in respect of Mr Miller?'

He recalled reading the SUI report and the Lamb report, but the Kemp report? Unfortunately, he could not recall reading it, stating: 'I think I didn't read it.' But he had corresponded with Mr Miller about it and had even sent him a copy of it.

'Why on earth are you sending an investigation report to a member of staff where you haven't read it?'

'I didn't feel I needed to read it in order to send it to him,' came the response.

'What possible basis can there be for you failing to read it when it makes the recommendations it does?'

'Because I didn't know how long the report was,' came the Medical Director's reply.

'Well, it's quite short isn't it?', the Coroner said, gesturing to it.

Failing to act on the Kemp report was a key missed opportunity to act sooner, according to the GGI. Another was the verbal feedback from Professor Neal. On the stand the Medical Director accepted that Professor Neal's report had been compromised by the Trust's failure to give context to his investigation, including failing to give him the Kemp and Lamb reports:

'He's not been given the tools to do a thorough job, has he?'

'Perhaps not.'

With regard to the verbal feedback Professor Neal had given to him and the Chief Executive, on the stand the Medical Director could remember the feedback about the trivial issue of prostate resection weights but unfortunately nothing else.

The Coroner continued: 'What was the next thing that alerted you to the fact that you, as Medical Director, needed to consider taking action?'

'When I met (*Mr and Mrs Patient A*) in January 2012,' came the reply.

As I sat there, I wondered if anyone would pick up on the fact that he had been alerted to patient C at the end of the preceding year, in December 2011. Had I had legal support, I would have slipped my lawyer a note or perhaps whispered to them to ask him on this point, but the moment passed, unchallenged.

What about all the patients in the red folder? All twenty-six of them with thirty-nine separate annotations by Professor Neal. He dealt with that by acknowledging that, although his attention had been drawn to them repeatedly, he hadn't appreciated that they were still a clinical risk:

'I think the thing that really crystallised it in my mind was when I had a conversation with Mr Swinn …who told me that for some of the patients who had been treated in a non-standard way that there was still a chance that they could have conventional therapy.'

What about the sets of notes that were given to him with a precis of the management stapled to the front together with a list of the specific concerns for each patient? He replied that he had not seen them.

The barristers moved on, and the subject came back to patient C. He was asked directly about the concerns raised about him in late 2011. There was a pause, then: 'I think concerns were raised with (*the Trust Cancer Lead*). I'm unclear if they were raised with me. I don't remember them being raised with me.'

This contrasted with the words of the Cancer Lead sitting in the same chair less than two hours before where he had stated the obligation he was under 'to escalate all concerns to the management team.'

Towards the end of one session of cross-examination by one of the family's barristers, he was asked a question: 'Do you think that yourself and other Medical Directors would benefit from mandatory training in investigating concerns of care by clinical staff?'

'Yes,' he replied.

He accepted criticism of the Trust's actions before he was appointed: 'Most actions between 2008 and 2010 were characterised by a request to Mr Miller to comply with the guidance and alter his practice accordingly. There was no appropriate follow-up to see if he complied with these requests. Is that accepted by the Trust?'

'I think it is a true statement. I accept it.'

He was asked if in hindsight he agreed that matters could have been brought to a head in 2010 when Philip Kemp wrote his report. 'In hindsight, yes.'

'Well, given that nobody seems to have given it very much attention in 2010 perhaps hindsight is inevitable,' came the icy response from the cross-examining QC. 'And you don't have any explanation for why your predecessor Medical Director didn't act on it, do you?'

'Well...(*he*) did act on it by including those patients in Professor Neal's review.'

Clearly, he had forgotten, or was unaware, that the Trust gave Professor Neal essentially nothing – the letters in the red folder had been put together by the nurses. I sat there frustrated at my lack of legal representation, meaning that another statement would pass unchallenged.

'Isn't the reality that the Trust had all the information that it needed in 2010 – to (*issue*) a report to the GMC, (*to ensure*) that Mr Miller be suspended in the interim and have these matters properly investigated?', the QC continued. 'It is incomprehensible that Professor Neal didn't have Dr Lamb's report. Agreed?'

The Medical Director's replies were ever more quiet. 'Yes,' came the response.

The QC pressed him further, stating that Professor Neal should have been given the notes of the patients concerned.

'Yes, I think having the notes of the patients for those concerned would have been helpful, and I think that certainly.' He was now agreeing with her.

Lastly, the Trust's QC cross-examined him. Again, the issue of when he was alerted to concerns about the management of patient C was raised. 'It may be suggested to you that in December 2011 concerns were raised with you about the care of patient C. Do you remember in December 2011 concerns being raised with you about the care of patient C?'

'I don't think I recall concerns being raised with me about (*patient C*) at that time.'

Next, it was the turn of the CEO to be called to the stand. The first substantive question from the Coroner was how long a handover he had received from his predecessor. 'The meeting was very brief. It was forty-five to sixty minutes long,' came the reply.

Large NHS Trusts are complex organisations with all sorts of issues – clinical, financial, staffing, safety, etc. – and for the incoming Chief Executive and Medical Director to have each met with their predecessors for perhaps a bit less than an hour seemed extraordinary.

As the line of questioning from the various barristers continued, the Chief Executive's defence strategy was clear. As expected, it was, in a nutshell, to claim not to have had enough evidence to act. He described the Trust receiving 'allegations without evidence' about Mr Miller's poor practice. My mind inevitably cast back to the long list of evidence we had provided.

But I was soon to discover that there was a more sinister strand to his defence. Presumably with the intention of undermining me and my statement, I would be personally attacked. I was characterised as someone with a personal grudge against Mr Miller whom, he alleged, I pursued. And he was happy to provide the court with a motive.

'Have you ever been of the view that Mr Swinn was motivated by professional jealousy?' Mr Miller's barrister asked him.

'Yes,' the CEO replied. Needless to say, he did not offer and nor was he asked to provide any evidence to back up this assertion.

He was next asked about the incident when Mr Miller had gone to the cricket at Lord's when he should have been at work. The Trust had repeatedly asked me to put this in writing to help their case against him. 'We need to dismiss him on conduct grounds, not clinical,' they had said.

'"Allegations without evidence"', Mr Miller's barrister said, echoing the CEO's phrase. He spun round and pointed at me. 'Brought to you by Mr Swinn... that (*Mr Miller*) was off at the cricket and you looked into that, and that was false .... you did an investigation and there was no evidence Mr Miller was there!'

I sat there, shocked and furious that my complying with the Trust's requests to make a statement would subsequently be used against me by the CEO in his written evidence to the Coroner, with the clear implication that I was making false allegations against Mr Miller in a blatant attempt to discredit me.

The words of Mr Miller's barrister hung in the air. How would the Chief Executive respond? Would he stick by his statement? Slowly, quietly, came his reply:

'It later transpired,' – he coughed and took a sip of water – 'that my understanding from (*the Medical Director*) through an additional investigation is that Mr Miller was at Lord's cricket ground.'

The Coroner interjected before the next barrister stood. '(*Chief Executive*), your statement is very clear... and your evidence has now changed because you said that it transpired that Mr Miller had actually been at Lord's cricket ground.'

After a pause, 'Yes... Mr Miller admitted later to (*the Medical Director*) that he had been there.'

'So wouldn't it have been wise to put that in', she snapped, 'because that paragraph as it stands seems to indicate that Mr Swinn had raised a concern which wasn't ever substantiated. That seems to be the suggestion,' she said.

'I didn't mean to suggest that to anyone, Ma'am,' came the rather implausible reply from the Chief Executive.

Had I been granted access to the legal bundle I would have been able to see and challenge some of the statements about me. But having legal support removed meant that I did not. In his written testimony, the Chief Executive had claimed that I went to his office early one morning to tell him that Mr Miller was going to the cricket that day when he should have been in the hospital. In fact, no such meeting ever took place and I was not even in the hospital on the day in question; the theatre logbook at Guildford showing I was there, thirty miles away, operating all day.

Frustratingly, like his Medical Director, the Chief Executive stated that he had not seen key documents such as the Kemp report, despite the fact that he had asked for it and had been given it, and key meetings, for example with the Cancer Lead and Mr Miller, could not be recollected. And nor could he recall my meeting with him in which I raised concerns with him regarding the Medical Director's inaction.

He conceded that, had the Kemp report been acted on, the GMC would have been contacted, at which point a proper investigation would have occurred.

'And that is why the Trust accepts that the Kemp look-back and the failure to act on it was a missed opportunity to grapple with the patient safety problem that there was and protect patients in 2010?'

'Yes,' came the clear reply.

• • •

A few days later, I was called to give evidence. I had not long settled into my seat when Mr Miller's barrister, Mr Boyle, projected on to a screen various documents for the court to see. They included exchanges between me and Mr Miller from 2006 designed to demonstrate a closer relationship between us than had existed, and formed part of a narrative that a subsequent souring of relations between us had led to my raising concerns about his practice.

The only problem was that I had never seen the documents before, and some had clearly been fabricated. One, purporting to have been written by me, included a misspelling of a nurse's name. Mr

Boyle asked me to comment on the document and I quickly pointed out the mistake, adding that, since I had been married to the nurse in question for sixteen years, I would be very unlikely to misspell her maiden name, and from that, together with a number of grammatical errors it contained, it was clear that I did not write the document and I had no idea where it had come from.

I was clearly disadvantaged by not being legally represented and I subsequently learned that I had every right to refuse to answer questions on the material because it had been disclosed to the court late the previous night and I had not been made aware of it. The questioning continued with aspersions being cast on my probity and character but I was able to defend myself adequately overall and in general stood my ground well.

Being cross-examined by the Trust's QC proved frustrating, not least because it proved impossible to say much of what I wanted to say – another consequence of not having my own lawyer: 'I am just going to cut you off a little bit,' and 'I'll see if we can cut to the chase.'

This was a shame because there was much I wanted to say. Before long came a leading question on an old, familiar issue: 'When you identified patient C had been mismanaged by Paul Miller, action was taken by (*the managers*) very swiftly, wasn't it?'

'No,' I replied. 'I cannot accept that, I am afraid, as the nurses raised the problem of patient C's management in December 2011. I had an email from (*the Medical Director*) in January 2012 saying that he had been alerted... and that it was being looked into.'

This clearly contradicted the Medical Director's assertion that he hadn't been notified about him ('I don't think I recall concerns being raised with me about patient C at that time.'), and was clearly an important intervention if it could be substantiated.

Towards the end of my time on the stand, the Coroner asked me to bring the email to court the following, summing-up, day. I therefore went that evening straight from court to my office in the hospital and spent some time trawling though old emails. I eventually managed to find the email in question and printed it off. It was sent to me from the Medical Director in January 2012 and clearly stated that he knew about patient C and that "The Trust is looking into it".

I arrived at court early the following morning, sought out the clerk of the court and handed it to him. I sat in the coffee room alone holding on to a plastic cup of steaming hot black coffee. Various people filed passed the open door on their way to their meeting rooms – families and legal teams of the deceased smiled a "good morning", but Trust staff with their legal team were keen to rush past the open door.

Mr Miller's barrister nodded hello as he passed and then came back and popped his head in.

'Good morning, Mr Boyle,' I said, holding his gaze. I still felt bruised from our encounter the day before and I had learned that being on the witness stand for several hours being cross-examined by numerous QCs does not aid sleep.

'Look,' he started, 'about yesterday. I hope you realise it's just the day job. Nothing personal.'

'Don't worry,' I replied. 'I know how these things work. No problem. Will you be in Manchester?'

He looked confused. 'Manchester?'

'Yes, for the GMC hearing.'

'Oh, that. No. I've managed to avoid that,' he said with a smile.

Just before 10 a.m., we all filed into a full court and I sat in my usual seat at the back. As it was the last day, more members of the press and family members of the deceased were in attendance. There was much legal debate between the Coroner and the row of lawyers regarding the email I had produced and why the Trust hadn't included it in their submitted material. Their explanation was that it was something to do with an IT problem in the Trust and was an entirely unintentional omission.

Then the Coroner said, 'I think we might have to ask Mr Swinn to take the stand again this morning.'

I really wasn't ready for this, and the pain I had felt the day before in the pit of my stomach instantly returned. The debate went on, but in the end the Coroner felt that, on balance, I need not take the stand again. I looked over at Kate and Catherine, who smiled and gave me a thumbs-up. The debate had taken most of the morning and we adjourned for lunch.

'All rise,' the clerk ordered as the Coroner entered the packed room at the start of the afternoon session. Silence descended, apart from the tapping on laptop keyboards by some of the press. When she read out her conclusions, there were no surprises and the families listened intently with great composure and dignity.

She found that all ten patients had suffered "suboptimal care" and criticised the Trust for failing to act. The deaths of three of them, she concluded, had been contributed to by neglect, adding: 'These findings point to a gross failure to provide basic medical attention.' These included patient A and patient C. In the case of a further three, including patient B, she concluded that there were 'missed opportunities' to identify the extent of cancer recurrence and provide treatment, causing life expectancy to be potentially compromised.

It was galling that all six patients had been flagged to the senior hospital management through a variety of routes – and some had even been among the ten patients studied during Philip Kemp's look-back exercise of 2010.

The Coroner found that 'senior managers were in my view aware of the potential risk to the safety of patients from an early stage, yet took no action. I heard evidence from the Trust that the allegations that were being made were unsubstantiated and we have heard a lot of evidence about this, yet they were slow to react, indeed sometimes not responding at all. The impression that I have got from the evidence is that all in all there did not appear to be any real appetite to follow the allegations through.'

Many of her key findings echoed those of the GGI report. Those pertaining to the Trust are listed in full below.

1. The Trust was ill-prepared to deal with staff complaints and the decision making appears to have been weighted in favour of protecting the clinician's reputation as opposed to patient safety.

2. The Trust were (sic) alerted to concerns about the conduct and competence issues relating to Mr Miller from 2008.

3. There were early concerns focusing on Mr Miller promoting HIFU and the non-compliance with preferred referral pathways.

4. The divisional leadership (and I would add leadership as a whole) between 2008 and 2010 did not take timely action. Requests were made to Mr Miller to comply with guidance and alter his practice but there was a failure to follow up his failure to comply.

5. There was an inadequate response to Mr Miller's failure to follow preferred referral pathways and MDT decisions.

6. There was a missed opportunity to act on the Chief Nurse (sic) report (that recommended that Mr Miller be suspended) in October 2011 as well as the external independent verbal report in March 2011. Although I accept that (the) subsequent report did not reflect that which he had said at the verbal meeting.

7. There was a failure by managers (and I would add senior managers) to follow up concerns and the whistle-blowing process or to report back their findings.

* * *

"Doctor and NHS Trust criticised over cancer patients' deaths" was the headline on the BBC news the following morning.

How would the Trust react? The Trust put out a communication from the Chief Executive that same day. It gave some of the Coroner's conclusions and expressed sympathies and apologies to the family and friends of those involved, but the concluding paragraph seemed misleading. In full, it stated: "We have worked hard to create the environment, systems and processes that ensure staff are supported to raise concerns, and that lessons are learnt and improvements made as a result. The culture of our organisation has been transformed, with the CQC rating us outstanding earlier this year".

Leaving to one side the hubristic tone regarding the CQC rating, anyone reading that might well infer that there had been a problem with raising concerns. My mind cast back to the time when the Chief Executive was on the stand claiming that there had been a lack of evidence. The cross-examining QC pointed out: 'Now, one of the problems was there wasn't actually a problem with speaking up. People did speak up. The nurses spoke up and the doctors spoke up, but their speaking up didn't get traction.'

• • •

Within weeks of the completion of the Coroner's inquest in October 2019, with its unambiguous conclusions, a number of colleagues reported to me conversations with senior managers in which responsibility for Trust failings were minimised or denied. A narrative was being spun, consciously or unconsciously, in which the managers sought to absolve themselves of responsibility by casting doubt on the validity of the GGI report and Coroner's conclusions.

I was told that the Chief Executive stated in a meeting with a group of Consultants that the Trust could not have acted sooner because they did not have enough evidence. There was the suggestion that we as whistle-blowers had not made our concerns clear and that we had not put them in writing, implying erroneously that they could not act. Presumably trying to paint me as some kind of nuisance and perhaps somewhat unhinged, the Chief Executive claimed that he 'even took Mr Swinn's calls a number of times at weekends.' This is despite the fact that I have never phoned him. Not even once.

What I was hearing was troubling and mirrored the letters I had previously received from the Trust management denying responsibility. I felt very strongly that, if the Trust was to improve and act better in the future if faced with a similar situation, then the first step had to be that it must admit and face up to its failings fully. I therefore took my ongoing concerns through various Trust processes, and this culminated in an interview with the Trust Deputy Chief Executive. Frustratingly but, at least in retrospect, entirely predictably, no significant progress was made because he was not in listening mode and chose to side with his boss, the Chief Executive.

I felt that I could not let it rest at that and so wrote to the Trust Chairman in January 2020:

> Dear (Chairman),
>
> I feel duty-bound to highlight to you my ongoing concern regarding the Trust's seeming inability to face up fully to the totality of its failings in how it dealt with the Paul Miller issue. Only by acknowledging them fully can it change and move forward. My concerns include:
>
> 1. That whilst the Trust publicly states that it accepts the GGI report, privately doubts are cast on its validity by senior managers.
> 2. Senior managers continue to say that the Trust could not have acted sooner than December 2013 as it did not have enough evidence. This beggars belief.
> 3. The treatment of those of us who were brave enough to raise concerns has at times been appalling and at times openly hostile.
> 4. The current situation is that clinicians elsewhere in the Trust tell me they have been put off raising concerns and I believe this is a clinical risk.
>
> I do not know what your involvement in this issue has been, if any. If you want to talk it through with me, please let me know. Equally, I would understand it if at this stage you would rather do your own research.
>
> Regards,
> Michael Swinn FRCS
> Consultant Urological Surgeon

Regrettably, the Chairman of the Trust did not wish to speak to me, let alone see me or hear anything more about what I had to say, instead replying: "…you might wish to meet (*the Senior Independent*

Director). I know you have spoken to (*her*) previously in regard to your case, and you may wish to discuss any of the points you have raised in your email to me with (*her*)".

Unfortunately, of course, it was this individual I had seen previously and who said the problem lay with us as whistle-blowers for not making ourselves clear. The Chairman knew this and, because there seemed little point in hitting my head against that particular brick wall again, I declined to reply.

CHAPTER 4

GMC

KNOWING THAT THE TRUST HAD REFERRED Mr Miller to the GMC in 2014, I was surprised midway through the following year not to have been contacted by them and so telephoned offering to help. I mentioned that I was surprised that they hadn't been in touch and was informed that they don't contact people asking for their opinion as they "are not allowed to go on a fishing exercise". After some basic questions as to my involvement with the case, they decided that I should be interviewed and this would be worked up into a statement. A date was agreed for a telephone interview, many weeks hence, on 20 October 2015.

A solicitor working for the GMC duly phoned. This proved to be a lengthy and frustrating conversation because she seemingly had no appreciable knowledge of medicine or the workings of hospitals, let alone MDTs, etc. Thus, much of what I said needed to be defined and explained. At any rate, she wrote down what I said and, when the conversation finished, said that she would get a transcript to me.

It arrived two weeks later but was full of errors and didn't really make much sense. I telephoned the GMC to say as much and, determined to get it right, agreed to be interviewed further. Despite undergoing further interviews on 9 November and 25 November, progress was frustratingly slow and yet another interview date was set up.

This became slightly ill-tempered when I pointed out that the GMC had been tasked with investigating Mr Miller more than a year before and yet were still struggling to accurately record the statements of witnesses. I was firmly put back in my place and told that by the solicitor that she needed to manage my expectations because 'if anything, Mr Miller will face some retraining.'

This was disconcerting but there didn't seem to be anything I could do other than get my statement right.

There were further lengthy telephone meetings regarding my statement with the GMC solicitor but, in March 2016, I sensed that we were not moving forward, and so decided to tear it up and start from scratch. I was contacted by a different solicitor from the GMC in August and met her later that month. I was aware that the Medical Director had also been asked to make a statement and, although its contents were of course unknown to me, I was concerned when he let slip to me one day that his was very short. I sensed mine might prove to be an important document and so worked hard on it. I gathered together much evidence to back up my stated concerns and included it all in what developed into a lengthy document, which I finally submitted in December 2016.

As part of their investigation, the GMC carried out a performance assessment. This was potentially important because it might feed into a future fitness to practice hearing for Mr Miller and entailed a team of six coming down to interview about five of us. When I went into the interview room, I was informed that I would be asked a standard set of questions and that my answers would be made available to Mr Miller.

The note-taker asked me to speak clearly and slowly and the interview began. I had taken a few notes in with me and referred to them occasionally. Similar to the GGI interview, I found it a cathartic experience, stating, with examples, exactly where I thought standards had been unacceptably low. While I was pleased that progress with the GMC investigation was now being made, I was dismayed by the amount of my resources it was sucking up. Not just time, although that was considerable, but the "head space" this issue was continuing to occupy.

Needless to say, the Trust had done nothing about the letter put before the Coroner which appeared to have been falsified. I had alerted the Medical Director to significant concerns about its authenticity the very day that I came across it, but the Trust had not been interested in pursuing the issue. At times, it felt as if the Trust was trying to minimise the significant problems there were – even if this meant ignoring flagrant issues such as this. On the stand, Mr Miller had been cross-examined on it and was repeatedly reminded by the Coroner of Rule 22 – that on the grounds of the risk of self-incrimination he had the right not to answer.

It was incomprehensible to me that the Trust seemed resolved not to confront the issue and, since I felt strongly that someone had to, I decided to email the GMC my concerns about the authenticity of the letter. This time, they responded quickly and wanted to know more. After a few email exchanges and telephone calls, a paralegal was dispatched to take a witness statement, and we met twice – on Monday, 20 May and again the following day. 'You know this will open up a whole separate investigation against Mr Miller?' he warned, and my heart sank.

The GMC investigation was undoubtedly becoming more complex and I guessed that they were waiting for the Coroner's hearing to conclude, but nevertheless it seemed ludicrously slow. The inquests finished in October 2019. A fitness to practice hearing about Mr Miller was arranged to take place in Manchester in November and December 2019 and I was given dates and times. Not much of a break after the Coroner's inquests, but perhaps best to get on with it.

Annoyingly, on 31 October 2019, I received an email changing my date, meaning that I hurriedly had to reinstate and cancel clinics and operating lists. Then, having just achieved that, the whole hearing was cancelled at short notice due to ill health. In January 2020, the GMC asked for availability between 17 July and 18 December 2020. A date was made for the hearing between 5 October 2020 and 18 December 2020, and I was asked to keep 5 October to 31 October free; dates which spanned the school half term. Unfortunately, the hearing was again cancelled just before – more ill health – and a plan was made to do it in February the following year.

I sat in the urology office at work a few days before, rereading my statement. I went through the chronology of the main events, the salient points of the clinical management of many of the patients and the areas of concern I and my colleagues had. I then looked at the key letter which I felt had been fabricated and went through it line by line, matching it to my statement on it. In my head, I rehearsed answers to potential questions and went over a list of reasons why I was concerned about it: the fact that it wasn't on the department's hard drive, the wrong font, the layout being wrong, the fact that neither I, nor the patient, received a copy, the fact that it did not contain any secretary's initials.

But something else didn't seem right. As I stared at it, I realised the fax number on the letter was wrong – by just one digit – but no official letter coming from the hospital would have the wrong number typed on the top because, of course, they were all templated. Also, the letter failed to include the patient's NHS number.

At a meeting with the GMC barrister and two paralegals on 17 February, I was asked to prepare and sign an additional supplemental witness statement about the letter. Over the next few days, there was then much toing and froing over the detail of my main statement and its attachments, but, finally, it all seemed set for me to take the stand on Monday, 22 February 2021.

Then, on Friday, 19 February, the GMC phoned me to say that Mr Miller's legal team was submitting new documents as evidence that they wanted to cross-examine me on. They were putting them before the tribunal and, as such, I would be given them beforehand. I had no idea what they were but asked for them to be sent them straightaway so that I could look at them.

'That's the thing. I'm afraid we haven't got them yet.'

'But I'm on the stand first thing Monday morning.'

'They say they will get them to you on Monday morning.'

Despite by now being a veteran of such events, I was nevertheless anxious the night before and did not sleep well, finally giving up – and getting up – at 5 a.m. I went over various possible questions and, still with no word on the documents, made my way to the hospital. There was the inevitable problem with the Skype connection but eventually it sprang into life and I was greeted by a smiling Cath, the GMC barrister.

'Have you received the documents from Mr Miller's team yet?'

'No.'

It was now after 9 a.m. and I was due to take the stand at 10 a.m. Then – at about 9.30 a.m. – I received an email from Mr Miller's legal team with an attachment of six documents totalling seventeen pages. The Trust's Head of Legal Affairs kindly brought me hard copies of them, which she had printed off upstairs. I then received another shock – a second attachment labelled "Bundle 2". I cautiously opened it to find a further twelve documents running to forty pages. So, a total of fifty-seven pages of documents to read, digest and prepare for cross-examination in half an hour's time.

I took a gulp of water and sucked on a mint as the view of the tribunal hearing room in Manchester came up on the screen in front of me. I explained that I had just received the documents and asked for some time – and it was agreed that the hearing would start a little late while I digested the contents of the documents, made notes and did my best to clear my thoughts.

From the very outset, Mr Miller's barrister was intensely adversarial. He questioned my authority to make a judgment on others' clinical practice. What's more, he added, I hadn't a special interest in bladder cancer and had never even written a paper on the subject. I spent the next several minutes informing him about my fellowship in Australia, my robotic preceptorship in Los Angeles, how I and others had set up the robotic cystectomy service at Guildford from scratch, now the busiest such centre in the UK. And the alleged lack of paper? I referred him to a copy of my CV, which included dozens of publications, including on bladder cancer. He went very quiet and I could see him on the screen shuffling papers as if searching for something else to talk about.

'It's gone very quiet there,' I said. 'Is everything alright? Is there a connection problem?'

I couldn't resist it.

'No, it's okay, Mr Swinn,' the Chairman responded. 'He's just thinking.'

'Oh, that's fine. Let me know when you're ready.'

Having got off to a good start, I gained in confidence and dealt with the next questions well and, after a pause for lunch, was invited to step down late afternoon, eight hours after having first arrived. As the days went by, Kate, Catherine and Abhay had their time on the stand and I was very sorry to hear that the nurses had been given a particularly tough time by Mr Miller's legal team.

Fitness to practice hearings occur in three stages. The first stage, so-called determination of the facts, finished in April, at which point the tribunal met in camera, handing down their determination on 23 July. At that point, a date was set for the tribunal to reconvene in October for stage 2 – to decide on impairment. Once that had been completed, the tribunal moved on to stage 3, in which any appropriate sanction is handed down, ranging from no action, through to suspension, calling for a period of retraining, and through to permanent erasure, i.e. "striking off". There were the inevitable delays but, on 14 December, the GMC telephoned me to say that the tribunal had just finished their deliberations and had concluded that Mr Miller's name be permanently erased from the medical register.

The fact that the Medical Practitioners Tribunal Record of Determinations ran to three hundred and forty-four pages bears testimony to the thorough and expert job that the tribunal members did. Almost all of the allegations were proved, including that of falsifying the letter put before the Coroner. They concluded:

"The Tribunal determined that, given the scale of Mr Miller's dishonesty, his deliberate disregard for patient safety, putting his own interests before that of his patients, together with a complete lack of insight and the significant risk of repetition, his conduct was irremediable and fundamentally incompatible with continued registration".

PART 4

Post Hoc Analysis

CHAPTER 1

Where did it all go wrong?

FROM THE PERSPECTIVE OF A WHISTLE-BLOWER, the whole experience I endured at the Surrey and Sussex Healthcare NHS Trust was one of more or less unremitting misery. For all the NHS's declarations of being open, transparent and receptive to whistle-blowers, the reality I, and I dare say many of my colleagues, encountered was the polar opposite.

The early days of raising concerns were met with indifference and incompetence. They were perhaps too busy in their day-to-day roles fighting fires elsewhere and did not have the resources or training to deal with concerns raised, however serious. They seemed to wish that the problems being brought to them were either not genuine or would somehow just magically disappear.

In retrospect, I was naive in trusting that the hospital managers would act, and it took a long time for the penny to drop that those in charge were simply ill-equipped to deal with the situation. As the GGI reported: "While there is evidence throughout the period 2008–2013 of management action following concerns raised, action was variously late and inadequate, either in strength of action taken or in the follow-up or closure of the issue".

I was far from alone in raising concerns – many others in the urology department did likewise – and there was also wide-scale reporting of concerns more generally. Line management routes were used by staff in urology, oncology and the wider surgical division to escalate concerns regarding both Mr Miller's conduct and patient management. These concerns included reports of promotion of HIFU, non-compliance with referral pathways, attendance, behaviour, cystoscopy practice, accuracy of the recording of patient consultations and behaviour towards medical and nursing colleagues, as well as patients. Thus, there were numerous strands of investigation going on in different parts of the hospital – the problem being that there was nobody in senior management with oversight.

Part of the explanation for this lies in the various tiers of middle management with unclear or unrobust reporting lines. The summary of events in previous chapters points to a relatively large number of individuals with partial knowledge of what was going on but with a lack of clear direction from above and a lack of clarity in their roles, which also, to a degree, overlapped. We therefore had the Clinical Governance Manager, the Risk Manager, the Cancer Manager and the Cancer Nursing Manager, in addition to the core nursing and medical management hierarchies, all involved but not communicating effectively.

The morass of middle management might have been more effective in dealing with the issues had proper records of meetings been kept. Unfortunately, all too often no notes were made at all at the meetings with managers at which concerns were explicitly raised. Perhaps the managers feared the risk of being criticised or challenged unless they had received concerns in writing.

As the GGI concluded: "There was a widespread belief amongst senior staff that there was a requirement for concerns to be raised only in writing if they were to be actioned, even though written policies did not require this directly or implicitly".

Had managers either ensured there was a written record of the meetings where concerns were raised or been prepared to act, knowing that concerns need not be put in writing, action may have occurred earlier. Some of these flaws might have been compensated for by a strong non-executive. The route to board level was not clear within the whistle-blowing policy, which contained nothing about the role of the SID or other non-executive director. Shockingly, the report found that when the NED Chair of the Quality Assurance Committee was alerted to problems surrounding Mr Miller, they selected to support the urologist in question. It is therefore entirely unsurprising that, in a system not having patient safety at the centre of decision making, patients came off worst.

This lack of focus on patients was, in my view, key to how events unfolded. Regarding Mr Miller's failure to follow referral pathways and MDT decisions, the GGI stated that "even after nursing and medical staff escalated these issues, the Trust failed to tackle them effectively. Whilst there were appropriate initial efforts taken on behalf of the Trust's senior management to raise this with Mr Miller, no one took overall responsibility for ensuring that he changed his actions accordingly".

At least part of the explanation for the Trust's inaction is stated in the next section in the report: "The review concludes that the issue of challenging a difficult and powerful personality outweighed concerns raised by a number of professionals".

The report found that the divisional leadership between 2008 and 2010 "did not take timely action, with most actions characterised by requests to Mr Miller to comply with guidance and there was no appropriate follow-up to his failure to comply with these requests". It concluded that "the balance of decision making was weighted in favour of protecting a clinician's reputation and credibility", with patient safety taking a back seat.

This last point, i.e. putting the clinician at the heart of their decision making rather than the patient, was not just a source of frustration that delayed progress; it acted as a catalyst. As the GGI put it:

"There was a strong feeling amongst those interviewed, which the (GGI) review team agrees with, that the Trust's failure to act early and appropriately in relation to Mr Miller actively encouraged his further non-compliance, with damaging consequences". And "The more protracted the period of perceived inaction, the more it appears that Mr Miller felt able to continue his non-compliant behaviour, with the effect that more patients were put at risk as a result".

When the Trust did get round to investigating the concerns, pretty much every aspect of the various reviews it commissioned was flawed. The report criticised the Trust's investigation processes generally, highlighting a lack of clarity at senior levels about how to select, assign and train investigators. They found a lack of review of the quality of investigations and a failure to include a mechanism for reviewing and adhering to timescales. They also found that the terms of reference were unclear and were, in fact, problematic, even for the reviewers themselves. They criticised the choice of reviewer for the internal review, making the point that this is critical, with best practice requiring the reviewer to have specialist knowledge as well as specialist investigative skills. The investigations suffered from a lack of senior managerial input to ensure staff cooperated fully with them. The selection of which recommendations made by the various reviews were to be implemented was "arbitrary at best, and the follow-up of implementation was hard to trace".

There seemed to us to be a lack of respect, almost a disdain for us whistle-blowers, which manifested itself in, among other ways, a failure to give us feedback regarding even the bare bones of the results of the various investigations we had triggered and to which we had contributed. This lack of feedback was not just frustrating for many of us at the time but was, the GGI found: "a key problem in this chain of events as it illustrates another opportunity where connections, themes and inconsistencies might have been identified and the case could have been dealt with at an earlier stage".

Following the IRM by the RCS, there was much work to be done: first of all, the look-back exercise of more than a thousand sets of notes. There seemed to be little cognisance among the hospital management that this was an immense job of work that occupied a huge amount of time, thought and effort. And I do not recall anyone from management coming down to see how we were getting on, let alone offer much needed time off or even moral support.

Similarly, when it came to manning the hotline following the inevitable fallout following the GGI report, Kate, Catherine and Cathy were merely handed a mobile phone with a request to make sure that one of them would be available to answer patient concerns, including on weekends. There was no training or direction given, nor again, any sense that there was an awareness of the trauma that those of us who were confronted with a large number of angry patients and relatives would experience. It really did seem during those times as if we had been left to our own devices. As one of us commented, 'It's as if they're saying, "it's your mess, now go and clear it up".'

In essence, on bringing concerns to hospital managers, not only were I and my colleagues repeatedly and roundly ignored, we were made at times to feel that we were being a nuisance, were perhaps part of the problem, and it was up to us to sort it all out. As the GGI put it: "staff who reported concerns were at times made to feel disapproved of by senior staff as though they were 'meddling in other people's lives' (meaning Mr Miller's). Many staff even reported a fear for the security of their jobs if they were seen to be 'making waves'".

As the years wore on, the Trust came under increasing pressure from the twin threats of litigation and adverse publicity, and the apathy that we had hitherto experienced developed into something more concerning. The Trust's determined efforts just days before the first set of inquests to force me to enter into court the precis of all ten cases, while telling me that I was to defend the Trust's position, adding casually that the Medical Director was pulling out because of personal reasons, was entirely unreasonable.

When I started openly criticising the Trust's handling of concerns, matters spiralled downwards. Once I had done that, it seemed that the Trust felt it fair game to criticise and attempt to undermine me. That some of the things they stated or implied about me were entirely untrue did not seem to bother them. I very much got the impression that they were on a mission to defend themselves at all costs and had judged that "muddying the water" might be helpful to their cause, irrespective of how it might affect me.

The inability of key senior managers to recall important events along the journey was enormously frustrating. A charitable view might be that some of this could be explained by genuine forgetfulness or perhaps the "memory illusion": the psychological phenomenon by which individuals protect themselves from the truth by believing a different version of it.

But it is more difficult to explain or forgive the Trust's removal of legal support for me by the time of the second set of inquests. This tactic left me more isolated than ever, unable to access the written statements of the Trust management, including the Medical Director and the Chief Executive. The lack of a legal representative also meant that I had no means of challenging what was being said in court. If only in the interests of getting to the truth, it cannot be right that a key witness to events that occurred in an NHS hospital was denied legal support in a Coroner's court by his NHS employers.

• • •

Undoubtedly, with its combination of indifference, incompetence, and worse, the NHS posed by far the greatest block to achieving a satisfactory outcome for patients in a timely manner. However, other aspects of the whistle-blower's experience are worth analysing.

Although the GMC and the Medical Practitioners Tribunal Service (MPTS) can be commended for their rigour, it should not be overlooked that it took seven and a half years from the time Mr Miller was referred to them for the GMC investigation and the MPTS's fitness to practice hearing to conclude. The frequent last-minute postponements to many meetings were problematic to all concerned and there will have been ramifications for the thirty or so witnesses involved, many of whom had cancelled other activities, including clinics and operating lists, in order to be free to give evidence.

Delays of the magnitude experienced in this case prolong the stress and anxiety for those involved. This affects patients and their families enormously, but also the doctor under investigation and the witnesses. The quality of witness testimony can diminish as the years go by because evidence may be more difficult to retrieve: people's memories tend to fade, enthusiasm may wane the longer it drags on and access to relevant evidential material may be compromised, for example, due to staff moving jobs. Stories of cases such as these going on for this many years can only act as a disincentive to those considering reporting an individual to the GMC, or even merely agreeing to act as a witness.

Similar frustrations came from the frequent delays to the pre-inquest hearings in the Coroner's court, followed by the change in format to allow all cases to be heard together. This was then compounded by an acceptance on behalf of the Coroner's service of the Trust's request for the whole hearing to be heard again a year later under a different Coroner.

Anybody considering raising concerns that might lead to giving evidence at a Coroner's inquest needs to be mindful of not only the huge amounts of time it will absorb but also the stress of entering into such an adversarial environment. I had taken an inquest at face value as being the fact-finding forum it is described to be – and was dismayed by the combative atmosphere, which included suffering personal attacks from my employer.

CHAPTER 2
What else might we have done?

THAT PROGRESS IN INVESTIGATING OUR CONCERNS was so stuttering and slow became more than merely a source of frustration for us as whistle-blowers; sadly, it resulted in more harm being done to patients. Inevitably, I ask myself what I and my colleagues might have done differently to bring matters to a head sooner.

It is very clear that we had at the very least a moral duty to raise concerns. Moreover, since 2012 the GMC's Code of Professional Standards has crystallised professional obligations with regard to such issues, stating: "All doctors have a duty to raise concerns where they believe that patient safety or care is being compromised by the practice of colleagues or the systems, policies and procedures in the organisations in which they work". The Code goes on to state how those concerns should be raised: "Wherever possible, you should first raise your concern with your manager or an appropriate officer of the organisation which employs you such as the consultant in charge of the team or the clinical or Medical Director or clinical governance lead responsible for your organisation".

Unfortunately, despite repeatedly pursuing precisely those routes, all the way up to and including the Chief Executive, our concerns were simply not adequately listened to or acted upon. Moreover, the repeated challenging of managers proved difficult and at times seemed counterproductive.

The most senior manager in a Trust, the Chief Executive, is responsible for everything that happens within it, and is therefore the individual who bears ultimate responsibility for doing the right thing. However, their reputation with the public and, perhaps more significantly, their political masters, is inextricably bound up with that of the Trust they lead: what is bad for the Trust is bad for them. In this context, they may not always be receptive to hearing concerns which they may rather view as being unfounded or perhaps the result of professional rivalries between employees. Thus, they might have to be actively persuaded into acknowledging a problem, which, the longer it goes on, will likely prove ever more difficult for them to face up to.

Sadly, it is clear that our experience echoes that of other whistle-blowers elsewhere. Former Health Minister and Liberal Democrat MP Norman Lamb, who has been active in supporting families in the Gosport case, has described how there was "an unwillingness by the NHS to face up to some really serious allegations about what happened in that hospital", where he judged there had been "a closing of ranks". Similar conclusions were drawn by the inquiries into Bristol, Morecombe Bay and Stafford Hospitals. The inquiry into the Paterson affair, chaired by Bishop Graham James, makes clear that there were "failings at every level of a dysfunctional health system when it comes to patient safety" and found that concerns raised by health care professionals in the NHS were missed on many occasions with managers failing to act because of "wilful blindness" leading to a "culture of avoidance and denial" that allowed Ian Paterson to "hide in plain sight". Dr Ravi Jayaram, Consultant Paediatrician at the Countess of Chester Hospital, told Manchester Crown Court in 2023 of the difficulty in persuading hospital managers that there was a problem with Lucy Letby, stating: 'We were getting a reasonable amount or pressure from senior manage-ment at the hospital not to make a fuss.'

Worse than being merely ignored, many people altruistically raising legitimate concerns have found themselves the target of criticism, conjecture and even censure. As Dr Stephen Brearey, Lead Consultant at the neonatal unit at the Countess of Chester Hospital, stated following Lucy Letby's sentencing to whole-life imprisonment for the callous murdering of seven babies: 'You go to senior colleagues with a problem and you come away confused and anxious.' Dr Brearey claimed that senior managers were worried about reputational damage to the organisation and that, instead of acting on their concerns, his and his colleagues' lives were made very uncomfortable. 'I can't emphasise enough how difficult a position that puts the clinician in: carrying out your clinical practice in that environment is very difficult.'

Ms Donna Ockenden's report into maternity failings at Shrewsbury and Telford Hospital NHS Trust, published in 2022, criticised NHS managers for the treatment of whistle-blowers and echoed many of the failings described by Dr Bill Kirkup CBE in his investigation into the failings at the maternity unit at Morecombe Bay, where he described a culture of bullying and a failure by the board to face up to problems. One staff member who tried to raise concerns was referred straight to occupational health. 'It seemed that as I dared raise a concern I must obviously be mentally unwell.'

So, if it is difficult, unproductive, or perhaps both, for a clinician to raise concerns with their line manager or senior executive, to whom can they turn? Freedom to Speak Up Guardians posts, created in 2016 after Sir Robert Francis's investigation into the Mid Staffordshire Hospital scandal, report directly to the Chief Executive of the Trust; an obvious flaw.

Perhaps I should have bypassed the executive and reported concerns to the SID? Unfortunately, my subsequent meetings with her, in which she chose not to accept my statements at face value but instead echo her Chief Executive's version of events that we had not raised concerns a sufficient number of times or at least not sufficiently clearly, shows that it would not have been productive.

What about bypassing her and going to the Chairman? Unfortunately, subsequent communications with him were equally unproductive – he did not wish to investigate the issue, nor even accept my offer to discuss it with him, choosing instead to direct me back to the SID with whom he knew I had previously had two unproductive meetings.

Sadly, it should be noted that my experience of dealing with the non-executive directorate is far from unique. At Morecombe Bay, for example, Dr Kirkup found the board to be "unaware and uninterested", and the only realistic conclusion to draw is that there was nobody at all within my organisation who was sufficiently equipped, or inclined, to bring the issue to a close sooner.

What about other health institutions external to the Trust? Bodies such as NHS England, the local Clinical Commissioning Group, the British Association of Urological Surgeons, the British Medical Association, and so on, are simply not geared up to help in such matters. A more plausible option would have been to notify the GMC of my concerns directly. Indeed, the GMC states that they should be contacted by doctors with concerns regarding patient safety where they have not been adequately addressed locally. But, even when the most senior doctor in the Trust, the Medical Director, made the referral to the GMC on the instructions of no less a body than RCS, it took more than seven years for the process to be completed.

Realistically, what chance would I have had as an individual reporting concerns to the GMC without the support of my employing hospital, whose leadership had itself in the early stages explicitly decided against the option of involving the GMC? The reality is that I would have been outnumbered and outgunned by the legal team of what would effectively have become the opposing side. While reporting directly to the GMC might in some ways have assuaged the "moral distress" that I and others were encountering, there are plenty of examples of doctors altruistically approaching the GMC in this way but finding themselves "in the dock", having to defend themselves against a series of counter accusations.

No matter how spurious those reactionary accusations might be, the resulting lengthy GMC investigations and potential for bad headlines are an unattractive proposition. After all, the advice of the Chair of the IRM of the RCS echoed in my mind from time to time: 'Whatever you do, make sure it's not you who reports him to the GMC as, if you do, you will create a whole lot of trouble for yourself.'

What about the other main health regulatory body, the CQC? How far would I have got with that? The role of the CQC is to monitor, inspect and regulate the treatment, care and support provided by a whole host of NHS services, including its hospitals,

GPs, dentists, ambulances, mental health services and care homes. Although the CQC offers to be the recipient of concerns, that is not their primary focus, and the number of misjudgments the CQC has made raises doubts in the minds of those who might turn to them about their ability to carry out a high-quality investigation.

For example, it positively praised the senior managers at the Edenfield Centre, a medium secure inpatient unit at Prestwich Hospital, noting its "strong, highly motivated leaders who carried strong vision and values". Giving it an overall rating of "good", the CQC stated that the staff "demonstrated the values of the Trust", which include being caring and compassionate, inspiring hope and showing respect.

In September 2022, the BBC's *Panorama* programme passed on to the CQC information about abuses it had captured in secret filming at the facility. This included footage of staff swearing at patients, mocking their self-harm, using restraint inappropriately and secluding patients for weeks in small, bare rooms. The CQC agreed with the BBC that patients were subjected to "inhumane and degrading" treatment. Christian Wakeford, the Labour MP, whose Bury South constituency includes the hospital, criticised the CQC's failure to act promptly and the inspectors' praise of leaders at the Trust. The mental health charity Mind told the BBC that the treatment and behaviour uncovered by the BBC at Edenfield "raises serious questions about the effectiveness of the CQC inspection process".

So much for the CQC's ability to inspect health care facilities. How do they respond to the alerting of safety concerns with them? Dame Jo Williams, former CQC Chair, has acknowledged failings on behalf of the CQC in how it dealt with whistle-blowers. Concerns were raised to both the NHS and the CQC regarding the mistreatment of residents at Winterbourne View Hospital in Gloucestershire. No action was taken until an exposé in 2011, again by BBC's *Panorama*, forced a change of heart that led to the hospital being closed and eleven members of staff being convicted of multiple charges of neglect and ill-treatment, with six going to jail. Dame Jo Williams said of the case: 'We did not respond as we should have and we have taken steps to put things right. Among other things, we set up a specialist team to deal with whistle-blowers and systems to make sure every such contact is followed up.'

So, is the CQC now equipped to deal with whistle-blowers effectively? Between 2015 and 2019, Mr Shyam Kumar, Consultant Orthopaedic Surgeon, raised serious concerns about patient safety to the CQC. He happened to work part time for the CQC as a special advisor on hospital inspections, and reported concerns to senior colleagues at the CQC regarding inadequate hospital inspections, staff bullying and serious patient harm. He also reported to them his concerns regarding a surgeon colleague, who was performing operations that were "inappropriate" or of "unacceptable" quality and which harmed patients. He also warned the CQC that the hospital management "wanted to bury it under the carpet". In addition, he drew their attention to a hospital inspection at which he claimed patient safety was significantly compromised when a whole group of whistle-blowing doctors was prevented from discussing their concerns.

And how did the CQC respond to Mr Kumar? They sacked him.

Mr Kumar took legal action against the CQC and won his case, the Manchester Employment Tribunal concluding that he had been unfairly dismissed. The tribunal noted that Mr Kumar's concerns had been justified, and their judgment was that the safety issues he had raised played a significant role in his dismissal, stating: "It is very clear that the emails and concerns raised by Mr Kumar played a significant role in his dismissal".

Mr Kumar said, 'I feel personally vindicated. I was perceived as a troublemaker within the CQC, or as a thorn in their side. That's what I believe. And they just ignored it.' The CQC responded by saying, 'We accept the tribunal findings and have learnt from this case.' They then went on to say, some might say unconvincingly, that they had already improved many of their processes.

Examples like this mean that many members of the medical profession would have no confidence in the CQC with regard to investigating serious concerns. In fact, informal discussions with numerous Consultant colleagues reveal that not one of them would have any confidence that an individual doctor reporting concerns to the CQC would result in a satisfactory outcome.

Exploring these other possible options does not change the obvious fact that the responsibility for investigating these matters clearly lay with the managers of the Trust, and, unless and until fundamental change takes place, the conditions will remain ripe for further NHS scandals to occur. In 2023, ten years after his damning report into the Mid Staffordshire NHS Trust, Sir Robert Francis said, 'One of the principal things that went wrong with Mid Staffs was the focus on targets but the real issue was that no one listened either to the patients or the staff. And I'm not sure we have made very much progress on that.' And the latest (2023) Freedom to Speak Up Guardian survey identified a sharp increase to sixty-six per cent of respondents citing that colleagues would not raise concerns due to a belief that their organisation would do nothing about it. Make no mistake: change is needed.

So, what should a whistle-blower do when he or she believes that significant harm is being done to patients and yet the most senior managers of the organisation, up to and including the Medical Director, Chief Executive and senior non-executive board members including the Chairman, are not listening or doing anything substantive? The answer is that we need a new body to which health workers can turn in such situations.

CHAPTER 3

Lessons from other industries

HOSPITALS ARE HIGHLY COMPLEX and innately risky environments. They can also be very busy: the NHS, the largest employer in Europe, treats one million people every thirty-six hours. Many of these interactions utilise sophisticated technology but, at the heart of health care provision, more so than perhaps in any other industry, are the fundamentally important person-to-person interactions between clinicians and between clinicians and their patients.

This human element confers a further layer of complexity and risk: different professionals have different skill sets, training, agendas, communication skills, and so on. And the truth is, people make mistakes. There are around five hundred "never events" per year in the NHS in which, for example, the wrong operation is carried out or perhaps the right operation but on the wrong side of the body. In 2020/21, the NHS paid out £2.2 billion in settlements for medical error. And, tragically, given the nature of the beast, some of these errors resulted in death.

At the start of this century, a report from the Institute of Medicine in the USA estimated that there were two hundred thousand preventable hospital deaths per year. Many studies since have been carried out in order to verify this figure and, while, inevitably, results vary depending on factors such as study design, all agree that the number of preventable hospital deaths per year in the USA alone can be measured in the tens of thousands.

The airline industry shares some common features with health care and has often been used as a comparator. Both rely on highly trained professionals using complex equipment in a potentially dangerous environment, and human factors are key in both industries. A further grim similarity is that the result of significant errors in both industries can be fatal.

During the early 1970s, analysis of a string of fatal air disasters showed some common contributory causes; key among them a loss of situational awareness. At the centre of this was often a senior pilot unwilling to accept advice or criticism from others; a problem compounded by junior pilots lacking the assertiveness, or being too frightened to speak up.

Prior to these incidents, the culture was centred around the pilot, and Captain Chesley Sullenberger ("Sully"), who famously successfully landed his Airbus A320 on the Hudson River in 2009, has described Captains at that time as "behaving like god with a small 'g' and Cowboy with a capital 'C." He described First Officers as carrying notebooks listing the idiosyncrasies and personal preferences of the different Captains they would work with in order to keep them happy. Comparison with Dr Richard Gordon's fictional Sir Lancelot Spratt in *Doctor in the House* seems inevitable.

Since that time, aviation has changed radically and by some measures it is estimated that airline travel today is eighty times safer than it was in the 1970s. Unfortunately, the same cannot be said for health care. Airline companies are now regarded as high-reliability organisations with an obsession with safety deeply embedded. In the world of commercial aviation, investment in radical change has resulted in a genuinely blame-free culture of reporting through a multitude of routes. Safety incidents are owned up to with the emphasis correctly being placed on investigating the system rather than the individual. As Matthew Syed put it in his book *Black Box Thinking*, there has been a shift from blame culture to one of learning.

This contrasts to health care where, all too often, under-resourced investigations are too narrowly focused on an individual, with inexpert investigations generating conclusions and actions which are, in turn, inadequately acted upon by senior managers, whose real motivation lies in protecting their and their hospital's reputation while having more than an eye on the finances.

The evidence from the airline industry is that breaking down outdated professional barriers has led to a more egalitarian environment and has facilitated speaking up about risk incidents. This has contributed to the creation of numerous different routes through which pilots can report concerns. Crucially, the systems have been created such that the individual raising concerns is de-identified, i.e. their identity is not apparent and cannot reasonably be ascertained from the information or data.

In the NHS, the persistence of hierarchies may make speaking up more difficult, as observed by pilot and health care safety campaigner Martin Bromiley, whose wife's tragic death was contributed to by rigid adherence to professional boundaries. But, crucially, the problems in the NHS are much broader and more deep rooted: a reluctance to speak out persists because it is anticipated to be time-consuming and there is a lack of confidence that speaking up will effect change. Moreover, there is considered to be a general lack of accountability for those who have transgressed and a concern that the lack of confidentiality will lead to recriminations for those who raised issues.

In the airline industry, the well-being and morale of staff are seen as key factors in a well-functioning team, and this contrasts sharply to the NHS, where the well-being of staff who have raised concerns is ignored at best. In fact, too often, whistle-blowers themselves become casualties of NHS managers, who undermine, discredit and intimidate them in their rush to defend themselves.

How did the airline industry manage to change so much? Analysis of past failings was key. Once it was recognised that a majority of air accidents historically was causally linked to human factors, the concept of crew resource management (CRM) was born. This is a way of working that recognises the importance of how people work together and concentrates on non-technical issues of communication, leadership and teamworking. All pilots undergo regular human factors training as part of CRM and, since its inception, there has been a dramatic reduction in air disasters. This contrasts to the NHS, where, astonishingly, there is no compulsory meaningful form of human factors training whatsoever.

Pilots are, of course, mandated by the Civil Aviation Authority (CAA) to spend regular periods training in a simulator, and this includes an assessment, not just of technical skills but also of how they interact with crew members. There is generally a three-yearly cycle to cover all manner of emergencies a pilot might come across, whether it be engine failure, a rejected take-off, air conditioning malfunction, etc. A pass is an absolute requirement and a temporary suspension of flying might be required pending retraining until a pass is achieved.

This is very different from the NHS where there is essentially no meaningful assessment of Consultants. While there is a system of annual appraisal to which Consultants are subjected, it is too often characterised as an irritating hurdle that can be overcome by a friendly chat with a like-minded colleague over a coffee.

In addition to simulator training, pilots undergo regular "live checks" through Line Operating Safety Audit (LOSA), during which a senior pilot sits at the back of the cockpit watching and assessing a pilot during a flight to check on their technical and also, importantly, their interpersonal skills. The concept of "audit" in the NHS is very different because its utility is restricted to the often rather dry analysis of clinical practice outcomes for which an individual Consultant might or might not be directly responsible.

What about a doctor's interpersonal skills? How are they assessed? Sadly, again, in the NHS the systems in place seem amateurish, unsophisticated and unhelpful when compared to the airline industry. In the NHS, the feedback to doctors from patients and colleagues about their performance is restricted to a short questionnaire that the doctor themselves asks a small number of individuals to complete once every few years. That the doctor selects which individuals to assess him or her breaks scientific principles of how to avoid sampling error. The inevitable bias in the responses negates any sense of the process being impartial and serves to make it largely a valueless exercise.

So, although a form of audit takes place in both industries, there exist no meaningful similarities between them, either in terms of the assessment of technical expertise or in the important sphere of person-to-person interaction.

In any event, through the flight data recorder (the black box), the aircraft monitors everything a pilot says and does. In the NHS, there is no routine audio-visual recording of clinical practice, and one wonders whether the time has come for closer supervision and recording of some significant clinical events, for example, major operations and outpatient consultations in which key decisions about treatment are made. Although some basic aspects of clinical practice in the NHS are measured and "recorded", such as length of stay, mortality rate and perhaps some complications, data is notoriously difficult to interpret due to all sorts of confounding factors outside of any doctor's control. Having a digital record of key clinical interactions would help reassure patients and would provide factual evidence of events.

The airline industry's policy of grounding pilots pending investigation makes sense. The comparison of my own experience with flying is to have me as co-pilot A raising concerns about the competence and probity of pilot B sitting in the next seat, only to have the manager tell pilot B that his co-pilot was making "serious allegations" about him while instructing them both to carry on flying the plane. Such an action would be utterly unthinkable in the airline industry due to the inevitable deterioration in the key working relationship between the two pilots. It would rightly be seen as potentially dangerous, irrespective of the merits or otherwise of the allegations themselves.

* * *

The finance industry serves as another useful comparator to the health care sector. Clearly, the stakes are very different – being merely pounds and dollars – yet these can represent the savings and pensions that vast numbers rely on. The various financial scandals in recent years in western economies have served to bring about much tighter regulation. This has happened not only at corporate level but also, perhaps since governments effectively underwrite the banks, at national level.

Similar to the airline industry, there is surveillance and scrutiny of employees' actions. Investment banks impose strict limits for traders: personal communications devices are banned from trading rooms and all telephone conversations are recorded. Emails are monitored and algorithms have been developed to detect concerning words or phrases.

Bank employees are encouraged to raise concerns through a variety of "speak up" channels, either through direct line management routes or through others, including directly to HR. When a reported issue appears to be sufficiently concerning to warrant a more independent view, it is investigated by an employee of the bank external from the immediate organisation and sometimes based in another country.

It is not unknown for traders arriving at their desk to be met by someone from HR and security, escorted out of the building and placed on leave, pending investigation. Such practice might be excessive in health care. However, with the NHS's lack of oversight of senior clinicians, coupled with its record of conducting investigations inexpertly, and particularly when, in the example of the IRM, the individual has to consent to be investigated, there seems scope for the NHS to take away something from such an approach.

Crucially, when an employee raises a concern, for example in an investment bank, their identity is protected and is not revealed to the individual about whom concerns are being raised. A demonstration of the degree to which the finance industry views the importance of protecting the identity of whistle-blowers is seen in the example of James ("Jes") Staley, former Chief Executive of Barclays Bank, who tried to identify the author of a letter sent to the company board in 2016 raising concerns about the recruitment of Tim Main as head of the bank's financial institutions group in New York.

Mr Staley used the bank's internal security unit to identify the author of the letter, whom he then accused of harassment. Mr Staley was exposed and paid a heavy price. Mark Steward, Financial Conduct Authority (FCA) Executive Director of Enforcement and

Market Oversight said, 'Whistle-blowers play a vital role in exposing poor practice and misconduct in the financial services sector. It is critical that individuals are able to speak up anonymously and without fear of retaliation.' Sam Woods, Chief Executive of the Prudential Regulation Authority (PRA), which, along with the FCA, replaced the Financial Services Authority (FSA) in 2013, said, 'Protection for whistle-blowers is an essential part of keeping the financial system safe and sound.'

Mr Staley was jointly fined by the FCA and PRA a total of £642,430. If he hadn't settled at an early stage of the investigation, he would have been fined £917,000. In addition, Barclays clawed back £500,000 of his bonus over the matter. Furthermore, New York's Department of Financial Services fined Barclays Bank PLC $15,000,000 because of Mr Staley's attempts to unmask the whistle-blower "in contravention of Barclays' established whistle-blowing policies and procedures".

The policy of clear and unambiguous support for whistle-blowers on the one hand and subsequent penalisation of poorly performing managers and the corporations for which they work on the other is light years away from the practice in the NHS. It is worth remembering that, in my own experience, my identity was revealed within twenty-four hours of raising concerns and was known widely within the hospital in days.

It is clear that the body which oversees and regulates the provision of financial services in the UK, the FCA, understands the value of raising concerns and positively encourages whistle-blowing, which it describes as "essential to our work". In recent years, it has expanded its dedicated whistle-blowing team, and its members have been highly trained to look at all the information submitted and to act on it appropriately.

In 2019, for example, they assessed 1,153 whistle-blower reports of 2,983 allegations. Every single concern raised to them is investigated and signed off at a senior level. Again, they understand the importance of protecting the identity of whistle-blowers, reassuring those contemplating raising concerns that "protecting the identity of our whistle-blowers is at the heart of what we do". The details of those raising concerns are stored securely, and access is limited to the whistle-blowing team. It is a given that the identity of the whistle-blower is withheld from the individual or individuals about whom the concerns were raised and, furthermore, the whistle-blower has the right to remain completely anonymous as the investigation progresses.

In comparison, the NHS consists of a highly complex series of disparate organisations with inconsistent leadership. There are courses and training programmes for its staff which are voluntary not compulsory. There is a culture which readily tolerates and defers to hierarchy. There is no regular assessment of technical skills, no compulsory training or assessment in human factors and no regular observation of performance once Consultant level is attained. Concerns are frequently not raised for fear of recriminations and the belief that they would be inexpertly investigated. Finally, those who raise concerns are aware that they will have their identity bandied about and may be a target for their NHS managers, casualties of the tactics used by those in charge in their rush to defend themselves.

Given all this, it seems hardly surprising, but nonetheless lamentable, that incidents of harm to patients in the NHS are as common as they are.

CHAPTER 4

Recommendations

COUNTLESS INDIVIDUALS AND THEIR FAMILIES were impacted by these events and, while nothing can make up for their loss, genuine acknowledgement of the failings accompanied by appropriate change can help make amends and, crucially, prevent similar situations occurring in the future. To embark upon this process thoroughly and thoughtfully also serves as a way of honouring the memory of those who suffered, and helps to repay, if only in a small way, the debt owed them.

It is therefore hoped that those in a position of authority who have in their gift the ability to bring about the changes needed heed the lessons learned and act accordingly.

In essence, the most basic shortcoming I encountered was the NHS's lack of focus on patient safety. This manifested itself in many ways, including the failure to take appropriate and timely action when faced with multiple individuals raising serious concerns. In aviation, with its checklists, preflight routines, black boxes, CRM, LOSA, multiple routes for the raising of concerns and their comprehensive investigation, serious incidents have become rare occurrences. At present, with its clinical targets, understaffing, patchy training and sometimes poor leadership, the NHS is, sadly, a world away from that.

But the NHS can change, and I would argue is obliged to do so. There needs to be a paradigm shift in its culture and systems to facilitate the embedding of safety right the way through its organisations from top to bottom, including at board level and financial decision making. To achieve this will require better training and regulation of managers, better treatment of whistle-blowers and the creation of a new, independent investigatory body to which whistle-blowers can turn in the event that local processes have been found wanting. Below, I discuss these and other suggestions, which I believe could form the core of the sort of changes that are needed.

Training of medical managers

An important step in achieving the NHS's transition to a high reliability organisation is improved training of medical managers. The leadership roles within hospitals carried out by doctors such as Head of Department, Chief of division (for example, surgery), and Medical Director, serve as vitally important cogs in the hospital machinery.

An individual in such a role will be responsible for overseeing and motivating perhaps scores of senior doctors across many different specialities. They will be responsible and held accountable for the clinical outcomes of the departments they oversee, act as a bridge between clinicians and Trust managers such as the Chief Executive, and help ensure targets are met within the financial constraints. Such jobs are challenging, stressful and time-consuming.

Unfortunately, all too often, inadequate resources are given to individuals in these roles, which are usually "piggy-backed" on to their day-to-day clinical roles. Typically, something like four hours per week is nominally set aside for these managerial duties, with a consequent increase in pay, which is too low to act as in incentive and which in no way represents fair compensation for the time, trouble and associated stress.

When it comes to learning how to deal with the inevitable challenging situations that arise – for example, as described in these pages – there is usually no formal training at all. In fact, there is no specific mandatory additional training for doctors before taking up the majority of such roles. In my view, the approach to, at the very least, the tier of medical managers at Chief of division level and higher, needs a radical overhaul.

All such doctors should be required to attend training on how to do the job, including, importantly, how to respond when faced with fellow clinicians reporting concerns. This mandatory training might lead to some sort of accreditation and would provide reassurance that, across the NHS, all medical managers above a certain level of seniority had been trained in at least the basics of how to fulfil their role. This should be underpinned by the allocation of an adequate amount of time to carry out their roles, including a reduction of clinical workload by perhaps half.

Until such changes are made, I am afraid that Consultants applying for such roles will continue to be small in number and frequently ineffective, with clinical risk being amplified as a direct consequence. We need to progress from the current situation, where these roles are performed by those who might reasonably be described as amateurs with varying degrees of enthusiasm, to a situation where such roles attract large numbers of highly trained, motivated individuals who compete for them safe in the knowledge that they will be supported by the Trust to fulfil their role to a high standard and will be compensated fairly for doing so.

Regulation of NHS senior managers

Doctors and nurses are tightly regulated by the GMC and the Nursing and Midwifery Council (NMC), respectively, and one of the duties of NHS managers is to refer underperforming clinicians to the relevant organisation. Being investigated by one's professional body is notoriously stressful and time-consuming, and is often associated with professional harm, even if the individual is exonerated.

Unfortunately, referral, or at least the threat of it to these regulatory bodies, seems to have been used as a weapon by some senior NHS managers to put pressure on clinicians to keep quiet. An NHS review at one of the largest Trusts in the country, University Hospitals Birmingham NHS Trust (UHB), described a "longstanding bullying and toxic environment", with Consultants further describing having been "punished quickly and harshly" for raising concerns, with one stating 'They will ruin your career.'

Eye surgeon Mr Tristan Reuser was referred to the GMC by UHB months after he had raised concerns about a lack of nurses to support operations at the Heart of England NHS Trust. The GMC exonerated him and commented that the referral by Chief Executive David Rosser "contained a number of material inaccuracies that suggest that David Rosser was deliberately misleading the GMC or, at best, that he had failed to give the matter anything like the level of care and attention required". Mr Reuser said that whistle-blowers at the Trust were subjected to 'victimisation and retribution', adding 'If you criticise senior management they will have you.' In the past decade, the Trust has referred twenty-six of its doctors to the GMC. In all cases, the GMC took no further action. By contrast, the GMC issued a formal warning against David Rosser, stating that his conduct "risked bringing the profession into disrepute and it must not be repeated".

Mr Reuser's employment tribunal found that he had been wrongfully dismissed by Chief Executive David Rosser, of whom the judge said, 'There is a strong suspicion of bias given his approval of the exclusion on grounds he ought to have known were false.' The Trust lost its appeal; the appeal judgment being equally scathing of the Trust's actions.

David Rosser was then subjected to a "fit and proper persons review": a test set by the CQC to help ensure minimum standards of behaviour among the NHS's leaders. Unfortunately, the review was carried out by a subordinate of David Rosser and found no fault. By contrast, a subsequent independent review into clinical safety at UHB stated: "In our opinion, statements made by the GMC and employment tribunal were extremely serious and brought into question David Rosser's suitability for senior leadership roles". It should be added that UHB have since changed personnel and recently acknowledged that serious mistakes were made, adding that they have strengthened governance and fit and proper procedures.

But what happens when senior NHS leaders are found wanting? Unfortunately, there is precious little accountability and all too often the chairperson of the Trust (Jacqui Smith, former Home Secretary) chooses to back their CEO and they continue in their role.

Alternatively, the individual concerned may sidestep into another high-paying NHS managerial role, thus dodging proper due scrutiny and missing the opportunity to learn the lessons that proper accountability might have brought. After leaving UHB, Dr Rosser was appointed the West Midlands first Strategic Director for Digital Health and Care. As former Health Secretary Jeremy Hunt observed, 'Too often managers who had failed were recycled to jobs in different parts of the country where they made the same mistakes.'

Another former Health Secretary, Stephen Barclay, commissioned barrister Tom Kark KC to carry out a review of NHS managers, and this was published in February 2019. The review concluded that all NHS managers should have knowledge of, among other things, how to respond to serious clinical incidents and of the value of raising concerns. He expressed the need to monitor, track and regulate managers, and advocated the principle that managers have an ethical duty towards both patients and staff. As part of this, he recommended setting up a body with the power to disbar directors for serious misconduct. To date, the government is yet to accept these proposals.

Better treatment of whistle-blowers

The inadequate training of medical managers and lack of regulation of senior managers in the NHS generally is, in my view, directly and inextricably linked to the scandalous ways in which whistle-blowers are treated in the NHS. Whistle-blowing should be actively encouraged, but the fact is hospital employees are currently extremely reticent to put their head above the parapet, and for understandable reasons.

The NHS ombudsman, Rob Behrens, recognises this, stating in an interview in late 2023 that "clinicians are stigmatised because they want to raise patient safety issues…NHS patients' lives will continue to be at risk until whistle-blowing law is changed". A key problem is the lack of anonymity accorded to those raising concerns. When I described my experience of having my identity widely known within the hospital within twenty-four hours of raising concerns, the senior training pilots and investment bankers I spoke to in researching this book responded with incredulity. Not only did that make life very difficult for me but, more importantly, since everyone in the department was expected to carry on working together as a team, further risk to patient care was generated.

Having one's identity revealed also serves as a powerful disincentive to anyone considering raising concerns. The raising of serious concerns about patient care should be regarded as a confidential matter between the whistle-blower and the senior management team, who have no right, in my opinion, to divulge the identity of the whistle-blower and, indeed, should have a duty to protect it.

If the culture in the NHS is to change then the role and welfare of whistle-blowers has to be recognised to a greater degree, as is the case in other industries. To this end, there needs to be a whole package of care directed towards a whistle-blower. Their anonymity needs to be protected and they need to be given time off to prepare for the inevitable reviews, interviews, tribunals and hearings that are likely to follow. They should be given the name of an individual in the Trust to whom they can turn for support and who will give their assurance that they will not suffer as a result of raising concerns. They also need to be assured that the Trust will look into the concerns promptly, thoroughly and fairly.

Lastly, an NHS Trust must never again be allowed to remove legal support for one of its employees who has been called as a witness to give evidence at the impartial, fact-finding process Coroner's hearings are supposed to be.

Lower threshold for suspending doctors

Once serious concerns about patient safety are raised, the hospital management should conduct a swift preliminary investigation to ascertain whether there is likely to be any substance to them. This would fall well short of being a full, definitive, investigation and would be conducted merely to see what the merits of the allegations are. If it was thought there was a reasonable chance, or greater, of patients being in harm's way, in the event that an individual doctor was responsible, he or she should be suspended from work immediately.

This would give the investigating team time to conduct a more in-depth investigation and prevent the individual corrupting evidence or attempting to "lean on" co-workers. It would also be safer, as the potential for further harm to patients would be eradicated, and would also be less unpleasant for those who had raised concerns.

The cultural shift in the NHS towards safety might therefore involve the more or less routine suspension of doctors for, usually, short periods of time. The emphasis would be that such relatively frequent, short suspensions would be required to ensure the safety and quality of a service or Consultant's practice and would therefore be much less of a stigma than is currently the case.

Mandatory logging of all serious clinical concerns

The online system for raising concerns in the NHS, Datix, has been around now for more than a decade. Thousands of reports are made every year in each Trust and there is a widespread feeling that any individual's report of a problem or near miss will get lost in the ether. Even if it does end up on the desk of one of the Trust's innumerable middle managers, the management system is so convoluted and opaque that clinicians have little confidence that action will ever be taken.

In fact, the raising of concerns in the NHS, for good reason, explicitly does not need to be put in writing. This is a sensible policy designed to make the raising of concerns less unattractive and, in my view, makes it even more important that managers log all serious concerns raised with them. Surely the time has come to change NHS policy to mandate the logging by managers of all serious concerns brought to them? By doing so, the scale and depth of the potential problem can be more easily assessed. I suspect that it would also make it more likely that managers would escalate concerns, ultimately to the Medical Director and the Chief Executive, who also would be more likely to act promptly and would be less likely subsequently to deny knowledge of concerns or their seriousness.

It is worth mentioning the context that many other industries scrupulously record adverse outcomes, near misses and the like. In the NHS it is standard practice for surgical departments to have a means for recording operative complications, no matter how trivial, for discussion at the relevant morbidity and mortality meeting. Hospital wards often have a book in which all manner of adverse events, such as wound or catheter infections or perhaps a patient or relative slipping on the floor, are recorded for subsequent discussion within the department. It is right that clinicians discuss and investigate such incidents but the contrast seems extraordinary that, when serious concerns regarding patient safety are raised to managers in the NHS, even including the reporting of patients' lives being at risk, no formal recording of those concerns is mandated.

Creation of a new, independent, external body to investigate concerns

Even if the NHS were to achieve a stronger safety culture, there will inevitably continue to be instances where an individual Trust gets it wrong by failing to listen or investigate adequately. In such a situation, who should the whistle-blower turn to?

The Freedom to Speak Up Guardians that were inserted into the hospital hierarchy in 2015 after Sir Robert Francis's inquiry into the Mid Staffordshire Hospital scandal are sadly often useless, since the holder of that position reports to the Chief Executive. If the Chief Executive is part of the problem – either because they have established the wrong culture in their hospital or because they are not responding appropriately themselves when concerns are raised – then Freedom to Speak Up Guardians are simply rendered impotent.

Sir Robert Francis remains concerned about the problem, acknowledging in 2023 that, despite it now being many years since his report, some whistle-blowers in the NHS continue to pay a heavy price, and he warned that protection for whistle-blowers may be insufficient to prevent another scandal like that at the Mid Staffordshire Hospital from happening again.

Even Dr Jayne Chidgey-Clark, the National Guardian for NHS England, i.e. the Lead Freedom to Speak Up Guardian, acknowledges the scale and seriousness of the problem, stating in 2023: 'I think at the moment there's lots of good work being done in some organisations to improve the speak up culture. But sadly, in some, there is still an absolute fear of repercussions. It is a real issue that we have to get right in the NHS.'

What is required is a new, independent, body, perhaps akin to the Independent Office for Police Conduct (IOPC) or FCA. Perhaps called something along the lines of the Independent Healthcare Concerns Commission (IHCC), it would be tasked solely with investigating serious concerns about patient safety once the internal organisational processes had been exhausted. Such a body would be created specifically for this purpose and this purpose only. As such, it would have in its DNA protection of the whistle-blower, and that means, if requested by the individual, withholding their identity even from the hospital where they work. This is vitally important in instances like mine, where not only was there nobody in a senior management position listening or with the skillset required to conduct a proper investigation but where they themselves became part of the problem.

The new body, perhaps the IHCC, would be the natural recipient of any and all serious concerns raised by health care staff once local processes had been deemed to have failed. It could be given powers to go into Trusts to carry out their work and would work closely with the relevant Royal College where appropriate.

Analysis by Protect, the whistle-blowing charity, showed that, in 2022, its helpline received contact from ninety-two NHS workers. Of those, a staggering seventy-seven per cent reported retaliation or detrimental treatment as a result of speaking up and thirty-three per cent said that they were either dismissed or felt that they had to resign as a consequence of raising concerns.

While the fear of raising concerns persists, and while internal processes in hospitals remain as poor as they are, NHS scandals will continue. That so many NHS staff with genuine concerns regarding patient safety resort to phoning a charity helpline for support should be regarded as nothing less than a national disgrace.

Revamp of the IRM

Perhaps the pivotal moment of this whole issue was the Invited Review Mechanism (IRM) of the RCS. This thorough piece of work, conducted by a small group of urologists and a lay person over a three-day period, agreed with the concerns raised, identified flaws in Trust practice and was instrumental in getting the investigation back on track.

However, as its name implies, any investigation team from the IRM has to be invited, and consent has to be given by the Consultant concerned. This last aspect seems an obvious flaw – and, indeed, in this case the IRM was refused some considerable time before. It is utterly unimaginable in the aviation industry that a pilot subject to allegations of unsafe, maverick practice could successfully refuse to be scrutinised by a group of his peers. Either the IRM mechanism should be compulsory or it should become standard practice to refer the individual concerned to the GMC in the event that they decline to give consent.

Limit the length of time of the GMC investigation and MPTS

Much of the early stages of the GMC investigation were slow, frustrating and of poor quality, including – and especially – the garnering of statements. However, the biggest problem was the length of time the GMC and fitness to practice hearing took: from referral to completion it was just short of eight years.

While, at times, there may have been understandable reasons for a short delay – such as the ill health of the doctor under investigation – there can be no excuse for it to go on as long as it did. After all, it is in nobody's interests to have extensive delays, least of all the victims and victims' families. Not only does a long period of investigation prolong the misery for patients and families (and the doctor under investigation) but, with the passage of time, the chances of a successful outcome are significantly diminished: witnesses retire, their memories fade, they move and might be uncontactable, they become ill or die and evidence itself becomes less easy to retrieve.

I believe, therefore, that consideration should be given to capping the length of time from referral to the GMC to completion of the process, including a fitness to practice hearing and the reaching of conclusions, at something like three years.

Enhanced training of Consultants to include human factors

But what about Consultants themselves? The lack of scrutiny of Consultants' practice seems extraordinary, especially when compared to pilots or those in the finance industry, for example. There needs to be human factors training with more of a focus on the cognitive and interpersonal skills needed to manage a team effectively. Surgery is a team-based activity, and scant – if any – training is delivered currently to facilitate the right environment.

Such training should, in my view, be embedded into the working lives of senior doctors with regular, frequent, compulsory classroom-based training, perhaps incorporating acting out different scenarios with paid professional actors, as happens in medical schools. This innovation would itself impress upon senior doctors the huge importance of teamwork in what they do. Such training modules should be compulsory with a satisfactory level of attainment being required to enable continued clinical practice.

Again, similar to pilots, I believe Consultants should undergo regular assessment in real time. That is to say that, for example biennially, every Consultant should be subjected to external scrutiny by a peer, perhaps a Consultant and a senior nurse observing. This might include an assessment of their technological skills and knowledge but also, crucially, of the way they lead their team and interact with nursing and medical staff. The assessors would be pulled from a pool of senior Consultants and nurses, perhaps those nearing retirement, with the breadth and depth of experience to conduct such assessments. One can envisage that these assessments might also include an anonymous questionnaire assessment to be completed by the wider team prior to the visit, which might itself be unannounced.

In summary, imagine a health care system with safety genuinely embedded in it at every level, and in which:

- Consultants are trained and assessed regularly in technical and human factors such as leadership and the importance of interpersonal working relationships;
- all employees are encouraged to speak up, safe in the knowledge that they will be listened to and have their identity protected;
- those raising concerns will be given time to prepare and attend any meetings and investigations, will not be attacked or blamed in any way by the hospital, nor suffer any professional harm in their organisation or the wider NHS;
- a team of well-trained managers, who record all serious concerns have the time, skillset and other resources to conduct a high-quality investigation in a timely manner;
- in the event that a preliminary investigation shows concerns to be associated with at least a reasonable level of expectation that patients are in harm's way, that the Consultant concerned is excluded to allow a thorough, fair investigation to take place;
- if the concerned individual believes there still to be significant clinical risk and has exhausted all local routes, they can report to the "Independent Healthcare Concerns Commission" or some such body;
- should a review of a Consultant's practice by the relevant Royal College be required, it would be compulsory on threat of referral to the GMC; and
- any GMC investigation and fitness to practice investigation is completed within a maximum of three years.

The essence of these suggestions is the prioritisation of patient welfare. To bring about meaningful change will require commitment, time and money. Some will say it would be too hard, too time-consuming and too expensive. Yet we all know in our heart of hearts that continuing as we are is not an option. Until or unless hospitals develop proper systems that can protect whistle-blowers, investigate matters promptly and effectively, and take action decisively, the danger remains that scenarios like my own will be just another in a long list of similar, tragic, scandals to blight the NHS.

Every Trust in the country is able to point to their website, triumphantly declaring how they encourage people to speak up and how open and transparent they are. But the reality is, these are just straplines – slogans designed to gain the moral high ground and reassure an unwitting public. We desperately need change, and we need to embark on that journey now. The numerous individuals and families at the heart of my – and other – stories, who suffered harm as a direct result, not just of medical mismanagement but of a system ill-equipped to listen to or act on numerous serious concerns, deserve nothing less.

Postscript

THERE REMAINED STRAINED RELATIONS with the senior management of the Trust, and I welcomed an invitation by the (new) Medical Director to meet up with him together with the (new) Chief Executive. On 1 March 2022, we duly met together with Kate and Abhay; Catherine was unwell. We saw it as an opportunity to set the record straight – to tell them in detail exactly what had happened and when.

We told them about the Trust failing to listen to early concerns from 2006, how they had failed to act on the Kemp report, how they had not listened to Professor Neal, how the Chief of Surgery claimed to the RCS not to have been aware of any clinical concerns, how the patients in the red folder were ignored by the Medical Director, how the Trust had removed legal support for me before the inquest, about the attempts to discredit me, how the Medical Director had somehow been unaware of the sets of notes in his office with typed concerns stapled to the front, how he could not remember the details regarding the index case, and so on. And yet how, despite all the evidence, they claimed to have acted appropriately at all times.

It was clear that much of what we said was new to them and they seemed genuinely shocked and saddened. The letter, below, written by the new Chief Executive, was received just over six weeks later; I guess because it had to be run past Capsticks, the Trust lawyers.

"I am so sorry to hear of the experiences you have had over a number of years in the organisation and the way this has left you feeling. I am particularly sorry to hear about the personal consequences to each of you as a result of your doing the right thing in raising concerns about the practice of one of your colleagues. Concerns which have been, as you say, totally vindicated.

It is clear to me from your feedback that we need to review our Whistle-blowing Policy particularly in relation to the reality of its implementation for the individuals involved. I would be grateful for your input into such a review as your experience will be vital in ensuring we get the governance process right from the perspective of the whistle-blower and the individual hearing the whistle-blower, and the package of support and access to information we need to ensure we put in place for the individuals involved. We recognise that there are some things (*the previous Medical Director*) could have done better, for example, his responsiveness to the red folder. However, it is clear from the evidence available that he acted appropriately in his management of key events in the timeline..."

I read the letter with a degree of relief but also much disappointment. She had, I supposed, conceded some ground, but it fell well short of the fulsome acknowledgement of the Trust's failings and apology that were warranted. Although she acknowledged that the Trust needed to review its whistle-blowing policy and requested our input in so doing, as I write these words more than a year later, nothing has happened.

Time will tell whether the new crop of hospital managers currently in place will facilitate a rebuilding of my relationship with the Trust. For now, there is an uneasy silence between us of the sort that might exist between a husband and wife after a row, and it does not seem possible that I could ever meaningfully contribute to the medical management of the Trust. For now, my focus and heart reside at Guildford, where over the last ten years we have built up a truly excellent bladder cancer centre of the highest quality and which has now carried out almost one thousand robot-assisted radical cystectomies; our current rate of work making us the busiest robotic cystectomy centre in the UK.

My mind frequently flicks back to the events of the last years and, however hard I try to rationalise it, given the wealth of evidence coming from different directions, I continue to find it astonishing that the Trust did not act sooner or more effectively. In a sense, I can just about understand it – no individual comes to work to do a bad job and the fault lines run through the culture, processes and practices of the NHS, rather than individuals. But what I find more difficult to come to terms with is their collective behaviour since.

I suppose we should not forget that, eventually, the Trust's intervention in arranging the IRM of the RCS did bring about an end to what was going on and perhaps it could all have been even worse – if, for example, the IRM had been even further delayed. But such notions are doubtless no comfort to the patients and their families who suffered harm and whose receipt of financial compensation will, of course, never adequately make up for their losses.

The trauma of it for the families involved is unimaginable. Some lost a father or mother, husband or wife, brother or sister. For those of us faithfully reporting concerns and being ignored or victimised, it has also been traumatic, although of course nowhere on the same scale. Nevertheless, the loss in terms of time, of spoilt holidays, poor health, poor sleep, lost career opportunities and broken or strained personal and professional relationships is, for me at least, incalculable.

It does not do to dwell on the losses; rather, I focus on the positives. First, the fact that I and others had a duty to speak up – we would have been complicit had we not, but also our actions prevented further potential harm. The letters and kind words I have received, principally from the families of those affected, have been much appreciated.

Part of what it is to be human is to expect an end to things: to an hour, a day, a job, a holiday, a life. We prefer neat endings but must accept that sometimes things end messily or at least unsatisfactorily. And so it is with this issue. The refusal by the Trust to accept its failings fully and its lack of progress in changing have put paid to any neat ending, at least for now.

But there are many similar accounts to mine, and the momentum for positive change in the NHS is building. Sometimes in the small hours over the years, I have found myself back in Jamaica discovering for the first time the joy and satisfaction of suturing a cut or setting a broken bone – the practice of surgery at its purest. And, in my mind, I see a system that works, simply by genuinely putting the patient at the heart of what it does. And the thoughts soothe like the cool sea breeze wafting through the open theatre door.

Olivia

IT IS A BRIGHT SATURDAY in spring and my eighteen-year-old daughter sits at the kitchen table. She has bought a book on how to get into medical school and is now on the section dealing with the interview. She is going through possible questions considering how best to answer them. Numerous pieces of paper are scattered on the table in front of her, seemingly in a state of disorderliness. I can see that each is adorned with copious scrawled notes in her own hand.

She looks up. 'Can I ask you a question?'

'Of course.'

'How do I answer it if they ask me what I would do if I had concerns about the practice of a fellow doctor? Do I just tell them I would tell the managers?'

'It's a bit more complicated than that,' I answer.

'How do you mean?'

'Unfortunately, the NHS isn't really up to dealing with individuals raising concerns. It doesn't have the right processes, training, expertise or resources.'

She stopped while she took in my words. 'You know the case you've been involved in for all these years? Would you do it again? Raise concerns?'

'Hopefully by the time you're a doctor they will be better sorted out, so the answer you should give them is that you would raise concerns and, in fact, you have a duty to.'

'But would you do it all again?'

I thought for a few moments.

'I really don't know.'

Printed in Great Britain
by Amazon

43320742R00126